Applied Algebra
Student Workbook

Marian Anton
Karen Santoro

All images created by Marian Anton and Karen Santoro, unless otherwise indicated.
Bugs, p.15, Leaf p.143-144 - Source: Used with permission of Microsoft.

Cover art created by Richard Uccello

www.kendallhunt.com
Send all inquiries to:
4050 Westmark Drive
Dubuque, IA 52004-1840

ISBN 979-8-7657-8086-2

Published in the United States of America

Table of Contents

Unit 0: Math Foundations in a Nutshell

0.1 Fundamental Arithmetic: The Integers

0.1 Numeration

I. Make a base 10 place-value chart up to hundred trillions. Label the periods.

In 1299 the City Council of Florence banned Hindu-Arabic numerals from financial records on the grounds that it was too easy to tamper with them. All numbers had to be written in words, and we do the same thing today on the rare occasions when we still write checks.

1. Write each number in words. Do not use digits. What might you do to the numbers first to make it easier?

a) 70345601

b) 95007450006

c) 800021000509582

2. Write each number using Hindu-Arabic numerals and commas for the periods.

a) *five trillion, forty billion, seventy-three million, four hundred sixteen thousand, two hundred sixty-five*

b) *fifty-six billion, three million, nine hundred seven thousand, ten*

c) *one hundred eight trillion, seven hundred thirty-nine billion, eight hundred forty million, five thousand, twenty-nine*

d) *seventy-eight trillion, twenty-two million, five hundred sixty-one thousand, three hundred*

e) *two hundred five trillion, sixty-four million, seven*

f) *ninety billion, two hundred fifty-nine thousand, seven hundred eight*

0.1 Rounding Counting Numbers

Given a number written in the base 10 place value system, we can round it by choosing any place value as a **level of rounding** and applying the following rules:

1. If the next lower-level digit is < 5 we **round down** by keeping the digit at the level of rounding the same, and making all lower-level digits zero. All digits above the level of rounding are left unchanged.

2. If the next lower-level digit is ≥ 5 we **round up** by increasing the digit at the level of rounding by one unit, regrouping the higher-level digits if necessary, and making all lower-level digits zero.

Round the given number to each specified level of rounding.

1. Round 24,857,250,529,596 to:

a) Ones.................................

b) Tens.................................

c) Hundreds...........................

d) Thousands........................

e) Ten thousands..................

f) Hundred thousands..........

g) Billions.............................

h) Trillions............................

i) Hundred Trillions.............

2. Round 409,057,650,195,932 to:

a) Tens...............................

b) Hundreds.......................

c) Thousands......................

d) Ten thousands................

e) Hundred thousands........

f) Billions..........................

g) Ten trillions...................

h) Hundred trillions...........

0.1 Addition of Counting Numbers

I. Describe what it means to add.

II. State **The Fundamental Principle of Addition (and Subtraction)** in your own words.

II. Use the addition algorithm to calculate the following sums. You may rewrite the terms vertically. (Why do that?)

1) $31 + 6$ 2) $43 + 19$ 3) $94{,}758 + 685{,}453$ 4) $69{,}832{,}679 + 350{,}189{,}536$

0.1 Subtraction

I. Describe what it means to subtract.

II. Use the subtraction algorithm to calculate the following differences. You may rewrite the terms vertically.

1) $38 - 6$ 2) $103 - 4$ 3) $75{,}412 - 22{,}518$ 4) $936{,}425 - 738{,}498$

III. Some schools teach addition and subtraction algorithms using 'carrying' and 'borrowing.' What do those mean in terms of regrouping units? Use examples to help explain.

Signed Numbers

1. What is the **opposite of a number**? Give examples to illustrate.

2. What other name is used for the operation of 'taking the opposite'?

3. Describe the set of **integers**.

4. Write subtractions as *additions* and regroup the positive and negative terms together. Then find the value.

a) $8 - 4 + 5 - 6$ b) $-12 + 3 - 5 + 4 - 1$ c) $30 - 13 - 8 + 5 - 2 + 10$

What is the advantage of changing subtractions to additions of the opposite? (Is $5 - 3 = 3 - 5$?)

5. Why are the operations of addition and subtraction called inverses of each other?

Modeling Addition and Subtraction

1. *In a garden, 59 tulips bloomed. Among them, 27 are yellow and the rest are purple.*
a) Draw a number-line model representing the situation, including units.

b) Name the operation and write a symbolic expression giving the answer. ____________________

2. *How far would a man be from his starting point if he advances 3 yards, and then goes back 8 yards?*
a) Draw a number-line model representing the situation, including units.

b) Name the operation and write a symbolic expression giving the answer. ____________________

3. *What is the net asset of a student who has 8 units of debt and 3 units of fortune?*
a) Use O for a 'debt' and X for a 'fortune' to create a visual model of this story.

b) Name the operation and write a symbolic expression giving the answer. ____________________

4. *The temperature reaches 10 degrees Fahrenheit during the day and it drops 15 degrees at night. What is the temperature at night?*
a) Create a visual model such as a number line or a O-X diagram for the story.

b) Write an expression using subtraction: ____________________, using addition: ____________________

5. *Mary is on floor 4 of a building while Jonathan is on floor* -3 *of the same building. Some buildings use negative numbers for floors below the ground level. How many floors does Jonathan have to go up to get to Mary's floor?*
a) Create a visual model such as a number line or a O-X diagram for the story.

b) Write an expression using subtraction: ____________________, using addition: ____________________

0.1 Multiplication

I. Describe what it means to multiply.

1. a) Write the repeated addition $9 + 9 + 9 + 9$ as a multiplication.

   b) Write the multiplication 3×7 as a repeated addition.

2. a) Draw an array with *5 columns of 3 bugs each.*
   (You can use an 'x' to represent a bug.)

   Then write a multiplication of the form
   (#columns) x (#bugs per column)
   to find the total number of bugs in the array.

   b) Draw an array with *3 rows of 5 bugs each.*

   Then write a multiplication of the form
   (#rows) x (#bugs per row)
   to find the total number of bugs in the array.

c) Are there the same number of bugs in each array? What property of multiplication can be deduced from this example?

II. Use the multiplication algorithm to calculate the following products.

a) 6×38 b) 46×103 c) $258 \times (-19)$ d) $(-71) \times (-34)$

e) $14 \times (-81)$ f) $(-752) \times 95$ g) 28×504 h) 498×316

Interpreting and Modeling Multiplication

Let $\boldsymbol{M}$ = the number of groups (abstract **M**ultiplier)
$\boldsymbol{N}$ = the number of units per group (concrete **N**umber)
$\boldsymbol{P}$ = the total number of units (concrete **P**roduct)

For each story, identify the concrete unit and the group.
a) Draw a number line model representing the story. Label the number line with units.
b) Write an equation of the form $\boldsymbol{M} \times \boldsymbol{N} = \boldsymbol{P}$ that answers the question.

1. *In Orchard A there are 6 cherry trees and in each tree there are 4 starlings (birds), and we are interested in the total number of starlings in the orchard.*

Concrete unit: Group: Equation:

Number line:

2. *In Orchard B there are 4 starlings (birds) and for each bird there are 6 cherry trees. We are interested in the total number of trees.*

Concrete unit: Group: Equation:

Number line:

3. *A crew travels in 5 vans with 10 passengers each. How many passengers are there in total?*

Concrete unit: Group: Equation:

Number line:

4. *If 1 meter of chain weighs 9 grams, how much do 7 meters of the same kind of chain weigh?*

Concrete unit: Group: Equation:

Number line:

0.1 Division

I. Describe what it means to divide.

1. a) Write the repeated subtraction as division. $36 - 9 - 9 - 9 - 9 = 0$.

   b) Write the division $35 \div 7 = 5$ as repeated subtraction.

   c) In the division $24 \div 8 = 3$, name the divisor, the dividend, and quotient.

II. Use the division algorithm to calculate the following quotients.

a) $4598 \div 38$

b) $245 \div 49$

c) $87{,}125 \div 425$

d) $41{,}366 \div (-481)$

e) $-13{,}992 \div 53$

f) $31{,}995 \div 45$

Interpreting and Modeling Division

Let $\boldsymbol{M}$ = the number of groups (abstract **M**ultiplier)
$\boldsymbol{N}$ = the number of units per group (concrete **N**umber)
$\boldsymbol{P}$ = the total number of units (concrete **P**roduct)

For each story, identify the concrete unit and the group.
a) Draw a number line model representing the story including units.
b) Write an equation of the form $\boldsymbol{P \div M = N}$ or $\boldsymbol{P \div N = M}$ that answers the question. Specify which it is.

1. *A child has 35 marbles in a bag and wants to share them equally among 5 of her classmates. We are interested in the number of marbles per classmate.*

Concrete unit: Group: Equation:

Number line:

2. *A child wants to share 35 marbles among her classmates, giving each of them 5 marbles. We are interested in the number of classmates that get 5 marbles.*

Concrete unit: Group: Equation:

Number line:

3. *One foot is 12 inches. If one piece of rope is 72 inches long, how long is it in feet?*

Concrete unit: Group: Equation:

Number line:

4. *If you drove 200 miles at a steady speed and it took you 5 hours, then how fast did you go?*

Concrete unit: Group: Equation:

Number line:

0.1 The Number Zero

Summarize the rules of arithmetic with zero. Let $\boldsymbol{a}$ be any number.

$a + 0 =$

$0 + a =$

$a - 0 =$

$0 - a =$

$a \times 0 =$

$0 \times a =$

$0 \div a =$

$a \div 0 =$

Which of the rules above do you think are most often remembered incorrectly? How will you be sure to remember?

0.1 Order of Operations

I. 1. How do the **first level operations** of addition and subtraction produce the **second level operations** of multiplication and division?

2. On which level is the operation of negation? Why?

3. Summarize the Order of Operation Rules for *evaluating* with the four basic operations: $+, \ -, \ \times, \ \div$

II. Use the Order of Operation rules to evaluate each expression WITHOUT a calculator.

a) $34 - 16 \div 4 + 19$

b) $50 \div 5 \times 2 \div 4 \times 9$

c) $(16 \div 2 - 16 \div 8) \div 3 \times 5000 - 2000$

d) $-(24 \div 3 \times 2 \div 2) - (30 - 10 + 5 - 1)$

0.1 Distributivity of Multiplication over Addition

I. *Suppose that we have 4 rows of 2 green bugs each and 4 rows of 3 black bugs each as in the diagram. We want to find the total number of bugs in the array, regardless of color.*

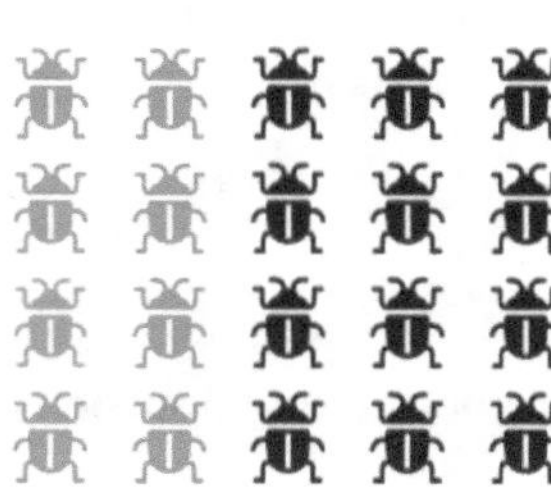

1. Write an expression to represent each step of each procedure.

Procedure 1: find the number of green bugs:

find the number of black bugs:

add the results:

Procedure 2: put together the green and black bugs in each row:

find the total number of bugs per row:

multiply the # of bugs per row by the # of rows:

2. Write an equation showing the equality of the two procedures.

II. Write the **Distributive Property of Multiplication over Addition**:

1) symbolically given (real) numbers $\boldsymbol{a}$, $\boldsymbol{b}$, and $\boldsymbol{c}$.

2) in words.

III. Use the properties of operations to evaluate the following expressions WITHOUT a calculator.

a) $-(12 - 3 - 5) - 2 + 1$

b) $425 \times 378 - 425 \times 377$

c) $-(4500 \div 100 + 5) - 20 + 10$

d) $6 - (-44) + 36 \div 9 \times 2 \times 10{,}000$

e) $9{,}000 \div 100 \times 2 \div (18 + (-12) - 6)$

f) $75 - (64 \div 32 \times 2) - 1 + 10$

0.2 Fundamental Arithmetic: The Rationals

0.2 Mental Math

I. Summarize the **Decomposition** Mental Math Strategy.

II. Summarize the **Compensation** Mental Math Strategy.

III. Use the *decomposition* strategy to perform each operation. Verify answers by performing the inverse operation.

a) $27 + 8$ b) $62 - 8$ c) $56 - 43$ d) $248 + 335$

e) 14×22 f) $828 \div 4$ g) 22×41 h) $1272 \div 6$

IV. Use the *compensation* strategy to perform each operation. Verify answers by performing the inverse operation.

a) $436 + 296$ b) $665 - 29$ c) $1298 - 50$ d) $874 + 25$

e) 9×24 f) 30×99 g) $45 + 39$ h) $277 - 29$

0.2 Divisibility of Numbers

If A, B, C are *natural numbers* such that $A \times B = C$, then C is a **multiple** of A and of B. At the same time, A and B are **factors** or **divisors** of C and we say that C is **divisible** by A and by B, or that A and B **divide** C.

I. List all of the natural **divisors** for the first 12 natural numbers.

Number	**Divisors**
0	
1	
2	
3	
4	
5	
6	
7	
8	
9	
10	
11	
12	

II. List the first 10 **multiples** for the first 12 natural numbers.

Number	**Multiples**
0	
1	
2	
3	
4	
5	
6	
7	
8	
9	
10	
11	
12	

III. Define each kind of number and list examples.

1. A **prime number**

2. A **composite number**

3. Which natural number is neither prime nor composite? Explain why.

State **The Fundamental Theorem of Arithmetic**.

IV. For each number, find the prime factorization.

a) 40 b) 125 c) 495 d) 60

e) 99 f) 240 g) 456 h) 2240

V. Given the two integers 18 and 24:
a) Find their natural divisors. Find all the common divisors. Which is the greatest common divisor?

b) List their positive multiples not greater than 300. Find a few common multiples. Which multiple is the least?

0.2 Launch: Part of a Whole

a) Work individually to shade *halves* of the rectangles below in as many different ways as you can. *Be creative!* Draw more rectangles if you need to. Put some samples on the board.

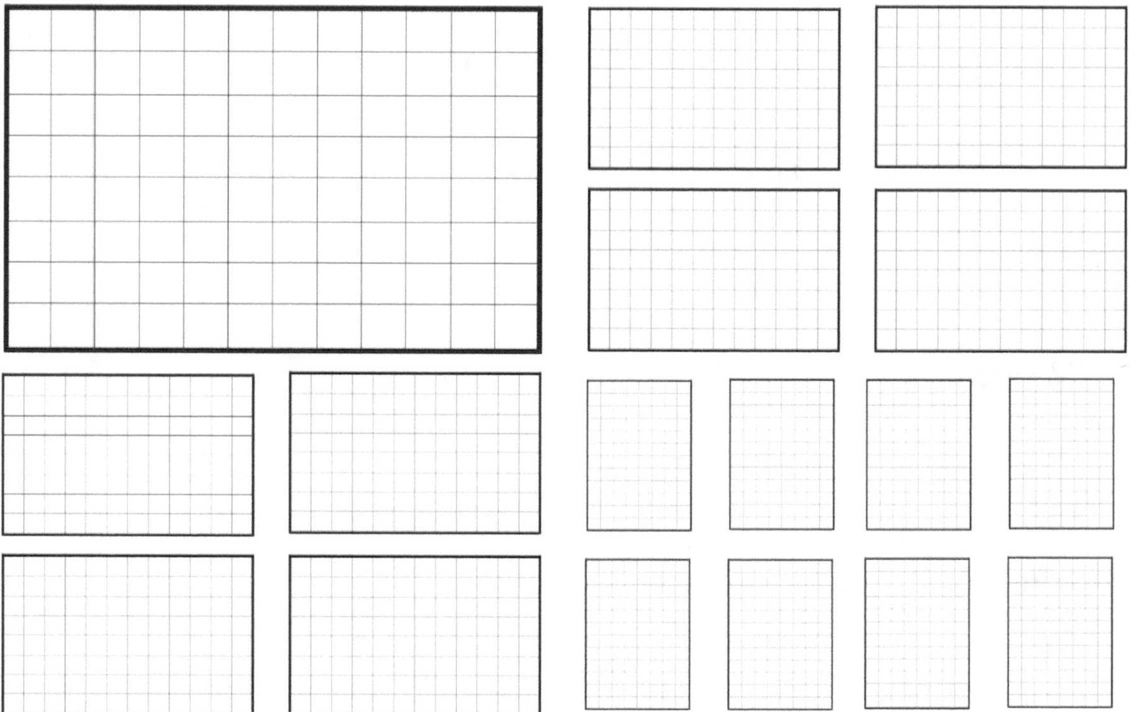

b) Discuss the size and the shape of the rectangles and their halves. Do halves have to look the same? Is a "half" always equal to a "half"? What is the whole?

c) Summarize the important ideas about fractions that came out of the Launch activity.

d) Fraction $= \frac{\text{Numerator}}{\text{Denominator}} =$ ______________________________

e) What is a **fractional unit**? Explain and give examples.

0.2 Ordinary Fractions

I. For each situation, identify the **fraction** described, then name its **whole unit** and its **fractional unit**.

1. Divide 5 apples equally among 6 children.

2. There are 7 people at a dinner party and there are two identical cakes to be shared equally among them.

3. One meter of chain weighs $\frac{5}{6}$ kilograms.

4. Gabriel spent \$240 which was $\frac{3}{5}$ of his paycheck.

5. Divide 3 cookies equally among 5 children.

6. Students on a road trip of 41 miles have 19 miles to go.

7. The child ate $2\frac{3}{4}$ cupcakes.

What is a **mixed number**? What are we 'mixing' in a mixed number?

II. Name the fraction represented by the *entire* shaded region given the specified whole.

1. The whole is the outer (largest) rectangle.
   a) 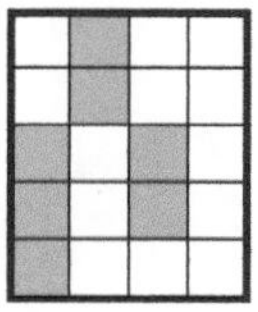
   b)

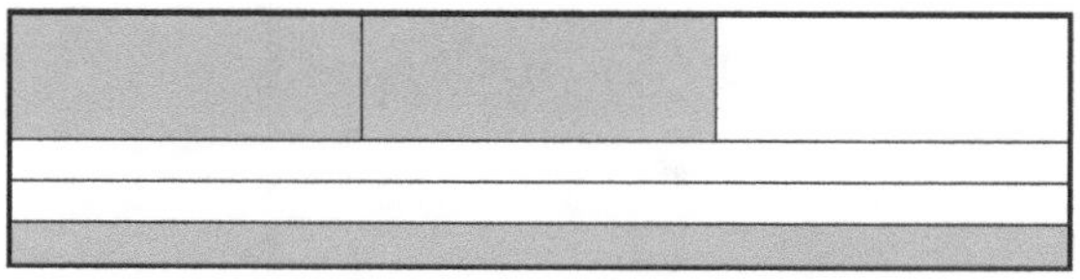

2. a. The whole is one large rectangle.

   b. The whole is two large rectangles.

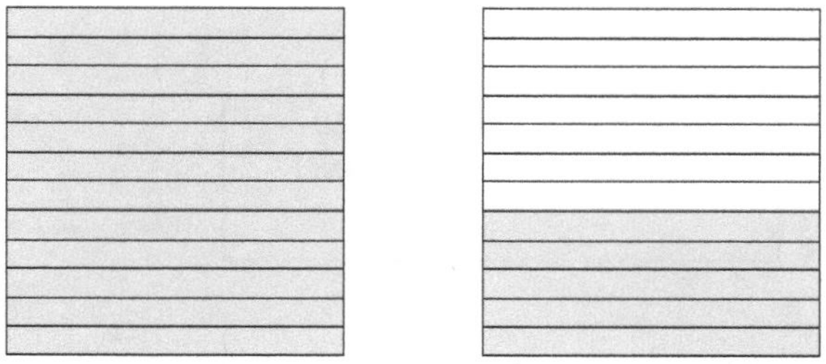

3. a. The whole is one large square.

   b. The whole is two large squares.

   c. The whole is all three large squares.

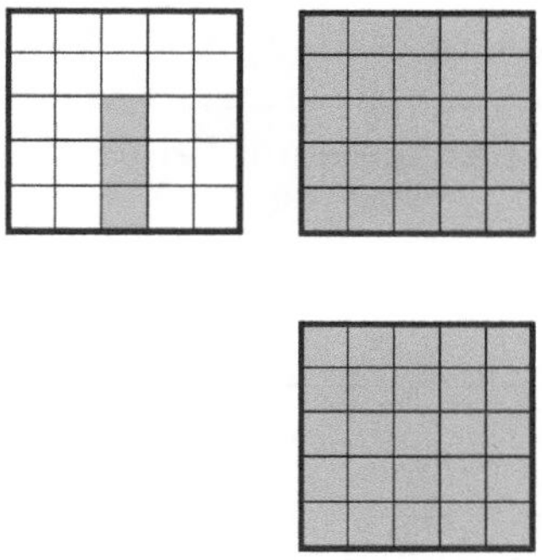

4. a. The whole is one large rectangle.

   b. The whole is two large rectangles.

   c. The whole is all three large squares.

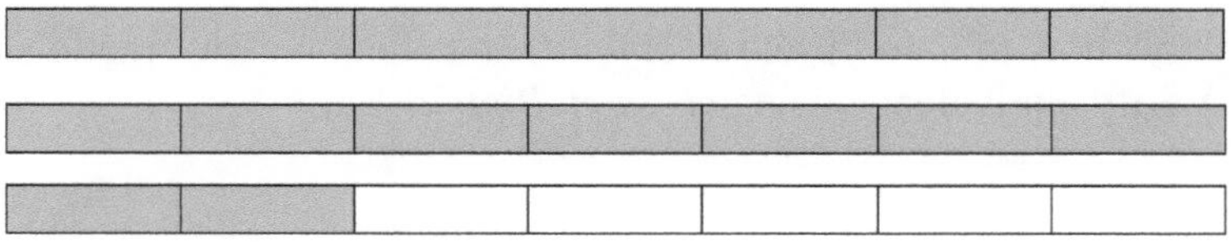

5. Describe the set of **rational numbers**.

III. **Equivalent Fractions**

1. What does it mean for two fractions to be equivalent?

2. Draw and shade rectangular area models to show the equivalence of the fractions.

a) $\frac{3}{4}\frac{\times 2}{\times 2} = \frac{6}{8}$

b) $\frac{4}{6}\frac{\div 2}{\div 2} = \frac{2}{3}$

$\frac{3}{4} =$

$\frac{4}{6} =$

$\frac{6}{8} =$

$\frac{2}{3} =$

3. State **The Fundamental Property of Equivalent Fractions**.

4. Explain why multiplying/dividing BOTH the numerator and denominator of a fraction by the same number gives an equivalent fraction.

5. For each fraction,
i. Show how to *amplify* and to *simplify* to get equivalent fractions algebraically if possible. If not, explain why.
ii. Verify equivalence using *cross multiplication*.

a) $\frac{1}{6}$

b) $\frac{4}{4}$

c) $\frac{3}{1}$

5. Continued:
i. Show how to *amplify* and to *simplify* to get equivalent fractions algebraically if possible. If not, explain why.
ii. Verify equivalence using *cross multiplication*.

d) $\frac{14}{35}$

e) $\frac{8}{0}$

f) $\frac{45}{63}$

g) $3\frac{2}{5}$

h) $\frac{0}{6}$

i) $\frac{30}{18}$

j) $\frac{9}{27}$

k) $\frac{40}{12}$

l) 5

m) $\frac{18}{36}$

n) $\frac{36}{12}$

o) $\frac{25}{125}$

6. Use prime factorization of numerator and denominator to simplify each fraction to lowest terms.

a) $\frac{90}{126}$

b) $\frac{432}{420}$

c) $\frac{330}{1100}$

d) $\frac{48}{120}$

IV. **Fractions on a Number Line**: Label the number line and use tick marks to show the location of each fraction.

a) $\frac{2}{3}$

b) $\frac{13}{3}$

c) $-\frac{3}{4}$

d) $\frac{13}{5}$

e) $-\frac{12}{4}$

V. **Comparing Fractions**: Use reasoning with a *common denominator*, a *common numerator*, or *benchmark fraction* to determine which fraction is greater. Explain your reasoning and insert the appropriate inequality symbol, < or >, between them.

1. $\frac{13}{5}$ $\frac{7}{5}$

2. $\frac{15}{7}$ $\frac{15}{11}$

3. $\frac{27}{25}$ $\frac{31}{33}$

4. $\frac{51}{100}$ $\frac{29}{60}$

5. $\frac{15}{14}$ $\frac{8}{7}$

6. $\frac{19}{6}$ $\frac{47}{15}$

7. $\frac{9}{133}$ $\frac{18}{265}$

8. $\frac{73}{35}$ $\frac{79}{40}$

0.2 Adding and Subtracting Fractions

I. Explain how the **Fundamental Principle of Addition** applies to addition and subtraction with fractions.

II. Fractions are equal parts of a whole. For each story, identify the whole. Then write an expression to answer the question and evaluate it. Label the answer with the whole unit.

1) *How big is a half pizza and a quarter pizza?*

2) *There was* $\frac{7}{8}$ *of a pan of brownies and then the family ate* $\frac{1}{4}$ *of the pan. How much was left?*

3) *Kim drove* $\frac{4}{9}$ *of the trip on the first day and drove* $\frac{1}{3}$ *of the trip the next day. How much had she driven in total?*

4) *There were 3 cakes at the party to be shared among 17 guests. Then someone brought another 2 cakes to the party. How much will each guest receive if the all the cake is shared equally?*

5) *We need* $2\frac{1}{2}$ *meters of fabric for one flag and* $1\frac{1}{4}$ *meters for another. How much do we need for both flags?*

6) The tailor had a piece of fabric $2\frac{3}{5}$ yards long and then cut off $\frac{1}{2}$ yard. How much fabric was left?

III. First estimate the result of each expression. Will it be more than 1 whole? Less? Will it be positive? Negative? Then evaluate the expression. Show all work.

1) $\frac{3}{5}+\frac{2}{3}$

2) $\frac{2}{3}-\frac{1}{9}$

3) $\frac{8}{6}+\frac{2}{15}$

4) $6-\frac{7}{8}$

5) $\frac{4}{5}-\frac{5}{4}$

6) $\frac{12}{7}+\frac{5}{3}$

7) $\frac{9}{8}-\frac{7}{10}$

8) $\frac{12}{7}+\frac{9}{14}$

9) $\frac{1}{8}-\frac{5}{6}$

10) $\frac{4}{5}+5\frac{2}{3}$

11) $2\frac{1}{4}-4\frac{1}{3}$

12) $\frac{17}{12}+\frac{3}{4}$

13) $8\frac{2}{15} - \frac{5}{12}$

14) $\frac{7}{9} - \frac{13}{36}$

15) $\frac{8}{25} + \frac{5}{3} - \frac{1}{5}$

16) $\frac{3}{20} - \frac{1}{5} + \frac{3}{4} + \frac{7}{6} - \frac{5}{3}$

17) $\frac{9}{10} + \frac{3}{4} - \frac{11}{6} - \frac{1}{3} + \frac{1}{2}$

0.2 Fraction Multiplication

I. Write the **Fraction Multiplication Rule**.

II. Evaluate each expression or explain why it cannot be evaluated. Show work and simplify final values if possible.

a) $\frac{7}{12} \times \frac{1}{2}$

b) $\frac{3}{4} \times \left(-\frac{2}{3}\right)$

c) $5 \times \frac{4}{7}$

d) $\frac{2}{3} \times (-18)$

e) $\frac{7}{8} \times \frac{4}{9}$

f) $\frac{2}{7} \times \frac{0}{6}$

g) $\frac{2}{3} + \frac{1}{5} \times 3$

h) $\frac{5}{7} \times \frac{7}{3} - \frac{1}{6}$

i) $\frac{3}{8} - \frac{2}{8} \times 8$

j) $10 \times \frac{15}{4} \times \frac{1}{10}$

k) $\frac{5}{6} \times \frac{6}{5} - \frac{1}{2}$

l) $\left(-\frac{2}{9}\right) \times \frac{6}{0} + 3$

III. What do we get when we multiply $\frac{2}{3}$ in different ways?

a) Shade $\frac{2}{3}$ of the (whole) rectangle (a).

a)

b) Multiply *the numerator AND the denominator* of $\frac{2}{3}$ by 2.
Show the result below, and shade that fraction of the rectangle (b).

b)

How does the new value compare with the original $\frac{2}{3}$?

c) Next multiply *only the numerator* of $\frac{2}{3}$ by 2.
Show the result below, and shade that fraction of the rectangle (c).

c)

How does the new value compare with the original $\frac{2}{3}$?

d) Finally, multiply *only the denominator* of $\frac{2}{3}$ by 2.
Show the result below, and shade that fraction of the rectangle (d).

d)

How does the value compare with the original $\frac{2}{3}$?

e) Summarize these findings.

IV. **Interpreting Multiplication with Fractions**

Recall the Interpretation of Multiplication $M \times N = P$, where

M = abstract **M**ultiplier (the number of wholes)

N = concrete **N**umber (the number of units per whole)

P = concrete **P**roduct (the total number of units)

For each problem, perform a unit analysis and write an equation of the form $M \times N = P$ to answer the question. You can evaluate in 2 ways: (a) using stepwise division and multiplication by integers, or (b) using fraction multiplication.

1) *If 1 kg of goods cost 20 dollars, how much does* $\frac{3}{5}$ *kg cost?*

Concrete unit: M: N:

Equation:

2) *A train travels* $1\frac{1}{5}$ *kilometers per minute. What distance does it travel in 4 minutes?*

Concrete unit: M: N:

Equation:

3) *If a serving of soda has 24 grams of sugar, how much sugar does* $\frac{5}{4}$ *of a serving have?*

Concrete unit: M: N:

Equation:

4) *A meter of chain weighs* $\frac{5}{6}$ *kilograms. How much does* $\frac{2}{3}$ *meter of the same chain weigh?*

Concrete unit: M: N:

Equation:

5) *Today we ate* $\frac{2}{3}$ *of the* $\frac{4}{5}$ *pan of brownies left from yesterday. How much did we eat today?*

Concrete unit: M: N:

Equation:

6) *A crew paved* $\frac{4}{5}$ *of a mile of road on the first day. The next day they paved* $\frac{7}{3}$ *of what they paved the first day. How much did the crew pave the second day?*

Concrete unit: M: N:

Equation:

0.2 Division by Fractions

I. Write the **Division by a Fraction Rule.**

II. Evaluate each expression or explain why it cannot be evaluated. Show work and simplify final values if possible.

a) $\frac{7}{12} \div \frac{1}{3}$

b) $\frac{3}{4} \div \left(-\frac{2}{3}\right)$

c) $\frac{9}{11} \div 3$

d) $6 \div \frac{1}{2}$

e) $\frac{5}{6} \div \frac{0}{5}$

f) $\frac{\left(-\frac{2}{9}\right)}{\left(-\frac{3}{4}\right)}$

g) $\frac{2}{3} \div \frac{(-1)}{5} \times \frac{3}{5}$

h) $\frac{24}{2+4}$

i) $\frac{3}{8} - \frac{3}{8} \div \frac{5}{8}$

j) $10 \div \frac{2}{5} \div \frac{1}{5}$

k) $\frac{7}{9} \times \frac{0}{3} \div \frac{2}{7}$

l) $\frac{20+35}{5}$

III. **Interpreting Division with Fractions**

Recall the Interpretation of Division $\boldsymbol{P} \div \boldsymbol{N} = \boldsymbol{M}$, or $\boldsymbol{P} \div \boldsymbol{M} = \boldsymbol{N}$ where

$\boldsymbol{M}$ = abstract **M**ultiplier (the number of wholes)
$\boldsymbol{N}$ = concrete **N**umber (the number of units per whole)
$\boldsymbol{P}$ = concrete **P**roduct (the total number of units)

For each problem, perform a unit analysis and write an equation of the form $\boldsymbol{P} \div \boldsymbol{N} = \boldsymbol{M}$ or $\boldsymbol{P} \div \boldsymbol{M} = \boldsymbol{N}$ to answer the question. You can evaluate (a) using stepwise multiplication and division by integers, or (b) using fraction division.

1) *If 3 kg of goods cost 45 dollars, how much does* 1 *kg cost?*

Concrete unit: ***P***:

Equation:

2) *If* $3\frac{1}{2}$ *kg of goods cost 35 dollars, how much does* 1 *kg cost?*

Concrete unit: ***P***:

Equation:

3) *If* $\frac{4}{5}$ *kg of goods cost 24 dollars, how much does* 1 *kg cost?*

Concrete unit: ***P***:

Equation:

4) *There is* $\frac{7}{8}$ *of a cake left over and it will be shared equally between 4 friends. How much does each friend get?*

Concrete unit: ***P***:

Equation:

5) *There was* $\frac{2}{3}$ *of a pan of brownies left over. If it is split up so that each friend gets* $\frac{1}{12}$ *of a pan, how many friends get* $\frac{1}{12}$ *of a pan?*

Concrete unit: ***P***:

Equation:

6) *A crew completed* $\frac{18}{21}$ *of a job. If each crew member completed* $\frac{2}{7}$ *of that part of the job, how many crew members were working?*

Concrete unit: ***P***:

Equation:

0.2 Decimal Fractions

I. What are **decimal units**? Describe them in words and give examples.

II. Make a base 10 place-value chart from hundred thous*ands* to hundred thousand*ths*. Label the decimal point.

III. 1) Use place value to say each number in words. (Hint: First identify the fractional unit.) Then write it in words.

a) 600.75309

b) 0.1004

c) 20.045

d) 1.00456

e) 0.900

f) 3.00001

g) 55.99

2) For each number, underline the decimal unit and then write the number in decimal form.

a) *five and four hundred sixteen ten-thousandths*..........................

b) *three hundred eighty three tenths*..

c) *one hundred and eight thousandths*..

d) *ninety four and sixteen hundredths*..

e) *eleven ten-thousandths*...

f) *twenty four tenths*...

g) *seven hundred sixty ten-thousandths*..

h) *fifty-six hundred thousandths*...

3) What are **decimal fractions**? Describe them in words and give examples.

In what two forms can we write them?

4) Go back to section III on the previous page and write each number as a decimal fraction with fraction bar.

5) Identify the decimal unit and rewrite the number as a decimal fraction with fraction bar. Simplify if possible.

a) 0.70 b) 2.1 c) 6.601

d) 0.0045 e) 2.00985 f) 30.008

g) 0.705 h) 0.0478 i) 0.0500

6) Write each fraction as decimal fraction with a fraction bar AND with decimal point. Show work.

a) $\frac{7}{4}$ b) $\frac{9}{20}$ c) $\frac{21}{35}$ d) $\frac{3}{5}$

e) $\frac{1}{8}$ f) $\frac{27}{50}$ g) $\frac{8}{2000}$ h) $\frac{45}{150}$

i) $\frac{7}{25}$ j) $\frac{18}{6}$ k) $\frac{21}{70}$ l) $\frac{26}{40}$

7) When can an ordinary fraction be converted into a decimal fraction?

8) What is a **periodic decimal fraction**? Give some 'better-known' examples.

9) Convert each number into a periodic decimal fraction written with a fraction bar. Show the division.

a) $\frac{1}{3}$ b) $\frac{17}{37}$ c) $\frac{1}{11}$

0.2 Rounding

Given a number written in the base 10 place value system, we can round it by choosing any place value as a **level of rounding** and applying the following rules:

1. If the next lower-level digit is < 5 we **round down** by keeping the digit at the level of rounding the same, and making all lower-level digits zero. All digits above the level of rounding are left unchanged.

2. If the next lower-level digit is ≥ 5 we **round up** by increasing the digit at the level of rounding by one unit, regrouping the higher-level digits if necessary, and making all lower-level digits zero.

Round the given number to each specified level of rounding.

1) Round 2025.0495 to:

a) Hundred-Thousandths....

b) Ten-Thousandths..........

c) Thousandths..................

d) Hundredths...................

e) Tenths..........................

f) Ones.............................

g) Tens............................

h) Hundreds......................

i) Thousands....................

2) Round 15.795055 to:

a) Hundred-Thousandths....

b) Ten-Thousandths..........

c) Thousandths..................

d) Hundredths...................

e) Tenths..........................

f) Ones.............................

g) Tens............................

h) Hundreds......................

i) Thousands....................

0.2 Percent

I. What is a **percent** representation of a number? Explain what it means and how to write it.

Why is using percent representations useful?

II. *We know that 420 out of 600 flowers in Euler's garden are roses and 480 out of 800 flowers in Newton's garden are roses.* Which garden has a greater fraction of roses? Use percent to answer the question.

III. Convert each ordinary fraction into a percent. Show work with equivalent fractions.

a) $\frac{2}{5}$

b) $\frac{90}{15}$

c) $\frac{5}{200}$

d) $\frac{17}{50}$

e) $\frac{13}{5}$

f) $\frac{12}{200}$

g) $\frac{9}{25}$

h) $\frac{42}{70}$

i) $\frac{11}{20}$

j) $\frac{300}{100}$

k) $\frac{4}{1}$

l) $\frac{33}{12}$

IV. Convert each percent into decimal fraction. Write it using a fraction bar AND with decimal point. Show work.

a) 13%

b) 2.4%

c) 140%

d) 0.02%

e) 7%

f) 5.5%

g) 300%

h) 0.4%

i) 82%

j) 100%

k) 125%

l) 22.8%

V. Convert each decimal fraction into percent. Use place value and show work with equivalent fractions.

a) 0.8

b) 1.2

c) 0.006

d) 3

e) 0.48

f) 0.008

g) 0.013

h) 0.265

i) 32.6

j) 7.046

0.3 Elementary Algebra: Expressions and Equations

0.3 Launch: Find the "Heap'

In the Ahmes papyrus [1550 BC] the unknown is called the 'heap.' Here is an example:

two thirds of a heap, one half of the same heap, and one seventh of the same make eleven. Find the 'heap.'

a) Guess the 'heap' by finding a number, say N, divisible by 2, 3, and 7. (Why?)

Your guess N:

b) Apply the operations to your guess N, and compare the result with 11. Did your guess work?

c) How can you modify your guess, N, to find the 'heap'? Do it and check your answer.

Is the 'guess-and-check' method of solving problems legitimate? Does is always work? What are some advantages and disadvantages of the guess-and-check' method?

0.3 Ratios and Proportions

I. What is a **ratio**? Explain it in words.

Give your own example of a ratio and show the different ways to represent it – with words, a colon, in fractional form, and with a double number line. Always label ratios with units.

II. What is a **proportion**? Explain it in words.

Use your example of a ratio in part (I) to write a proportion.

What does it mean to say that two quantities are **proportional**?

III. For each problem,

- Draw and label a double number line. Mark the origin, the given ratio, and the unknown.
- Write a proportion to represent the problem.
- Solve the proportion algebraically with cross multiplication or equivalent fraction methods amplification and simplification.

1) *A cook uses salt and sugar in the ratio* $9:2$ *for a pasta sauce recipe. If he uses 45 grams of salt, how much sugar will he use?*

Double number line:

Proportion:

2) *There are 4 times as many children as adults at a park. If there are 72 children, how many adults are there?*

Double number line:

Proportion:

3) *There were 5 cats for every 3 dogs at the shelter. If there were 36 dogs, how many cats were there?*

Double number line:

Proportion:

4) *At a farm the ratio of chickens to geese is 25 to 7. If there are 150 chickens, how many geese are there?*

Double number line:

Proportion:

5) *A biker travels 7 miles in a half hour. At that rate, how many miles will she travel in* $3\frac{1}{4}$ *hours?*

Double number line:

Proportion:

6) *A boat is going* $\frac{3}{4}$ *of a mile every 3 minutes. How long does it take to travel 1 mile? 2 miles?*

Double number line:

Proportion:

Proportions for Percent

7) *On a test with 120 questions, Kyle got 84 questions correct. What percent of the questions did he get right?*

Double number line:

Proportion:

8) *A study shows that 20% of 40 dentists prefer Super W toothpaste. How many of those dentists prefer Super W?*

Double number line:

Proportion:

9) *$15,000 is 3% of what amount?*

Double number line:

Proportion:

10) *A ship has sailed 270 miles. If this is 45% of the voyage, how far is the total trip?*

Double number line:

Proportion:

11) *A coin tossed 1230 times lands on tails 246 times. What percentage of tosses came up tails? Is it a fair coin?*

Double number line:

Proportion:

Proportions for Fractions

12) *Find a line segment such that* $\frac{3}{4}$ *of its length is 6 meters.*

Double number line:

Proportion:

13) *How much does a container hold if it is* $\frac{2}{3}$ *full with 144 liters?*

Double number line:

Proportion:

Proportions for Conversions

14) *Convert 30 inches to feet.*

Double number line:

Proportion:

15) *Convert 135 minutes to hours.*

Double number line:

Proportion:

16) *Convert 4.6 hours to minutes.*

Double number line:

Proportion:

17) *Convert 75 minutes to hours.*

Double number line:

Proportion:

Derived Proportions

I. *Suppose there are 5 black pens to every 3 red pens.*

a) Write the ratio in fractional form and label it with the quantities.

b) Make a triple number line where the 3rd line represents the total.

c) Write as many derived proportions from the triple number line as you can. Label them with the quantities.

II. For each problem,

- Draw and label a triple number line. Mark the origin, the given ratio, and the unknown.
- Write a *derived* proportion to represent the problem.
- Solve the proportion algebraically with cross multiplication or equivalent fraction methods amplification and simplification.

1) *There are 3 adults for every 5 children at a block party. If there are 18 adults, how many people are at the party altogether?*

Triple number line:

Derived Proportion:

2) *In a box there are 5 blue pens for every 3 red pens. If there are a total of 72 pens in the box, how many pens of each color are there?*

Triple number line:

Derived Proportion:

3) *At a lunch there was a choice of pizza or tacos. Three times as many students chose pizza over tacos and all together 180 ate lunch. How many students had pizza? Had tacos?*

Triple number line:

Derived Proportion:

4) *Mixing apple and grape juice in a ratio of 4 to 3 makes Ali's favorite juice mixture. How much grape juice does she need to make 105 cups of the mixture?*

Triple number line:

Derived Proportion:

5) *There are 7 penguins for every 3 seals at the aquarium. If there are 112 penguins, how many penguins and seals are there altogether?*

Triple number line:

Derived Proportion:

6) *The ratio of SUVs to cars in a parking lot is 8 to 3. If there are 275 SUVs and cars in the lot altogether, how many are cars?*

Triple number line:

Derived Proportion:

7) *An object is moving uniformly at 75 feet per hour. Find the distance traveled by the object in 90 minutes.*

Triple number line:

Derived Proportion:

8) *A pool is filling at a steady rate of 12 gallons per minute. How much water is added in 2.25 hours?*

Triple number line:

Derived Proportion:

9) *A homeowner installs 9 inches of paved walkway every hour. Find the length she can install in 210 minutes.*

Triple number line:

Derived Proportion:

10) *A homeowner takes 80 minutes to install one foot of paved walkway. How long will it take her to install 75 inches?*

Triple number line:

Derived Proportion:

0.3 Mental Math with Percent

I. Find each percentage of the whole using benchmark percentages and mental math strategies. Make a table with the benchmark percentages of the whole to help.

1) Find 16% of $200.

100%	$200
50%	
25%	
10%	
5%	
1%	

2) Find 6% of $80.

100%	
50%	
25%	
10%	
5%	
1%	

3) Find 24% of $64.

100%	
50%	
25%	
10%	
5%	
1%	

4) Find 30% of $45.

5) Find 15% of $140.

6) Find 60% of $480.

7) Find 75% of $280.

8) Find 9% of $2400.

9) Find 125% of $860.

10) Find 150% of $90.

11) Find 20% of $6250.

12) Find 325% of $32.

13) Find 15% of $12.60

14) Find 65% of $286.

15) Find 16% of $5400.

0.3 More Proportion Problems

For each problem,

- Draw and label a double or a triple number line. Mark the origin, the given ratio, and the unknown.
- Write a proportion to represent the problem.
- Solve the proportion algebraically with cross multiplication or equivalent fraction methods amplification and simplification. You must show work but you may use your calculator on these problems.

1) *A dessert recipe that serves 8 people requires 2¼ cups of sugar. If you make the recipe using 13½ cups of sugar, how many people will it serve?*

2) *A certain pre-school has a 3 to 4 ratio of girls to boys. There are 159 girls in the school. How many boys are in the school?*

3) *2 packs of roofing shingles cover 65 square feet. How many packs are needed to cover 1365 square feet?*

4) *Zach is on a road trip. The total trip is 1224 miles. He drove the first 442 miles in 6 ½ hours. At that same average rate, how long will it take him to drive the last 782 miles?*

5) *Marisa reads 18 pages in 30 minutes. How many hours will it take Marisa to read a book with 324 pages?*

6) *You bought 6 gallons of premium gas for $ 24.66. How much will it cost you to fill an empty 20 gallon tank with the same kind of gas?*

7) *Kaylon can read 18 pages in 20 minutes. At that rate, how many pages will Marisa read in 2 hours?*

8) *A certain pre-school has a 3 to 4 ratio of girls to boys. There are 392 total children in the school. How many boys are in the school?*

9) *A scaled drawing of a building uses 1/4 inch for every 1 foot. If a wall measures 13.5 inches on the drawing, what is the actual length of that wall?*

10) *Kenesha is on a road trip. She drove the first 442 miles in 6 ½ hours. At that same average rate, how far will she drive in the next 45 minutes?*

0.3 Powers and Radicals

I. Describe what it means to raise a number $\boldsymbol{b}$ to the $\boldsymbol{n}$th power, $\boldsymbol{b^n}$. Demonstrate with a numerical example.

What is another name for this operation?

What is the special name for a number to the 2nd power? To the 3rd power?

II. In the exponential expression $5^3 = 125$, name the base, the exponent, and the power.

III. Fill in the table with some the powers that are useful to know. How many did you already know?

$2^0 =$	$2^1 =$	$2^2 =$	$2^3 =$	$2^4 =$	$2^5 =$
$3^0 =$	$3^1 =$	$3^2 =$	$3^3 =$	$3^4 =$	
$4^0 =$	$4^1 =$	$4^2 =$	$4^3 =$	$4^4 =$	
$5^0 =$	$5^1 =$	$5^2 =$	$5^3 =$	$5^4 =$	
$6^0 =$	$6^1 =$	$6^2 =$			
$7^0 =$	$7^1 =$	$7^2 =$			
$8^0 =$	$8^1 =$	$8^2 =$			
$9^0 =$	$9^1 =$	$9^2 =$			
$10^0 =$	$10^1 =$	$10^2 =$	$10^3 =$	$10^4 =$	$10^5 =$
$11^0 =$	$11^1 =$	$11^2 =$			
$12^0 =$	$12 =$	$12^2 =$			

IV. How thick is a piece of paper folded 10 times if its initial thickness was 0.1 millimeters?

0.3 Rules of Exponents

I. Expand each power into products and simplify. Let $\boldsymbol{a}$ and $\boldsymbol{b}$ be real numbers $\boldsymbol{b \neq 0}$.

a) b^2b^3

b) $\frac{b^2}{b^3}$

c) $(b^2)^3$

d) $(ab)^3$

e) -5^2

f) $(-5)^2$

g) $-(5)^2$

h) -5^3

i) $(-5)^3$

II. 1) Explain why $-9^2 = -81$ *but* $(-9)^2 = +81$.

2) Explain why $-4^3 = -64$ *and* $(-4)^3 = -64$.

III. Expand each expression. Then simplify and/or evaluate it.

a) -7^2

b) $\left(\frac{5}{2}\right)^3$

c) $\left(\frac{7}{9}\right)^2$

d) $(-11)^2$

e) -5^2

f) $(-2)^3$

g) $(-2)^4$

h) $7(-2)^3$

i) $(2^3)^2$

j) $\left(\frac{4}{3}\right)^3$

k) $10(3)^2$

l) $5(2)^3$

m) a^3a^5

n) $(a^2)^3$

o) $7(10)^4$

p) $(3^2)^4$

q) 5^25^3

r) $(b^4)^2$

s) $\frac{2^5}{2^3}$

t) $\frac{7^2}{7^4}$

u) $\frac{b^7}{b^3}$

0.3 Negative Exponents

I. Explore the pattern of positive and negative powers of 2 in the table.
First fill in the table going forward with positive exponents.
Then reason backwards; reverse the table to show the meaning of negative exponents.

Expand	Value		Value	
$2^{-5} =$				
$2^{-4} =$				
$2^{-3} =$				
$2^{-2} =$				
$2^{-1} =$				
$2^{0} = 1$	1	$\times 2$	1	$\div 2 = \times \frac{1}{2}$
$2^{1} = 1 \times 2$	2	$\times 2$	2	$\div 2 = \times \frac{1}{2}$
$2^{2} = 1 \times 2 \times 2$	4		4	
$2^{3} =$				
$2^{4} =$				
$2^{5} =$				

II. Explain what negative exponents mean in your own words. Demonstrate with another example. (Not base 2)

III. The Equator is 24,901 miles long, and a pencil is 7.5 inches. If we repeatedly halve the equator 28 times, which one is longer, that length or the pencil?

III. Expand each expression. Then simplify and/or evaluate it. Let $\boldsymbol{a, b \neq 0}$.

a) 7^{-2}

b) $\left(\frac{5}{2}\right)^{-3}$

c) $\left(\frac{7}{9}\right)^{-2}$

d) $(-11)^2$

e) -5^{-2}

f) $\left(\frac{3}{4}\right)^{-3}$

g) $\left(\frac{5}{7}\right)^{-4}$

h) $(-2)^{-3}$

i) $(2^{-3})^2$

j) $\left(\frac{4}{3}\right)^{-3}$

k) $10(3)^{-2}$

l) $5(2)^{-3}$

m) a^3a^5

n) $(a^{-2})^3$

o) $9\left(\frac{9}{5}\right)^{-6}$

p) $(3^2)^{-4}$

q) 5^25^{-3}

r) $(b^4)^2$

s) $a^{-5}a^2$

t) $b^{-3}b^2$

u) 10^{-5}

0.3 Fractional Exponents

I. 1) What is a **fractional unit**?

2) What is the fractional unit $\frac{1}{3}$ of the whole 12? Show this as an algebraic expression. What operation is it?

How can you show $\frac{1}{3}$ of the whole 12 visually?

How did you break up the whole of 12 to take $\frac{1}{3}$ *of* 12?

If instead of breaking up a number into equal parts by addition as we did above with the whole of 12, we can break it up into equal parts by multiplication. In other words, we can break it into n equal factor parts. Taking one of these equal factors gives us the **fractional unit $\frac{1}{n}$ power** of a base.

3) What is the fractional unit $\frac{1}{3}$ *power* of the whole 64, $64^{\frac{1}{3}}$? Evaluate by writing the base as a product of equal factors and taking one of those parts.

Evaluate $64^{\frac{2}{3}}$.

II. Evaluate each fractional power by writing the base (whole) as a product of equal factor parts and taking the required number of those parts. Then evaluate the power.

a) $25^{\frac{1}{2}}$

e) $(16)^{\frac{3}{2}}$

i) $\left(\frac{49}{81}\right)^{\frac{1}{2}}$

b) $(-27)^{\frac{1}{3}}$

f) $27^{\frac{4}{3}}$

j) $\left(\frac{27}{1000}\right)^{\frac{2}{3}}$

c) $\left(\frac{1}{32}\right)^{\frac{4}{5}}$

g) $100{,}000^{\frac{6}{5}}$

k) $27^{\frac{2}{3}}$

d) $(81)^{\frac{3}{4}}$

h) $9^{\frac{3}{2}}$

l) $\left(\frac{625}{16}\right)^{\frac{1}{4}}$

III. Write a **radical** symbol and explain what means. What is the **index** of a radical?

How are radicals related to exponents? Illustrate with numerical examples with a variety of indices.

What special name is there for a radical with index of 2?

With index of 3?

IV. Go back to section (II) on the previous page and rewrite each exponential expression as a radical expression.

V. For each expression,

- *Re*write it - as an exponential expression.
- Expand the base as a product of equal factors.
- Evaluate the expression.

1) $\sqrt[3]{8}$

2) $\sqrt[3]{27}$

3) $\sqrt[5]{32}$

4) $\left(\sqrt[4]{16}\right)^3$

5) $\sqrt{\frac{25}{49}}$

6) $\left(\sqrt[3]{64}\right)^2$

7) $\sqrt[6]{1{,}000{,}000}$

8) $\sqrt[3]{-125}$

9) $\left(\sqrt{\frac{4}{9}}\right)^3$

10) $\left(\sqrt[4]{16}\right)^5$

11) $\left(\sqrt[3]{-125}\right)^3$

12) $\left(\sqrt{-4}\right)^6$

VI. Explain why taking the nth $root$ of b is the **inverse** operation to taking the nth $power$ of b for $b > 0$ and $n > 1$ natural. Give some numerical examples to illustrate.

VII. 1) What is an **irrational number**? How do they relate to fractional exponents and radicals? What are some examples of irrational numbers?

2) Describe the set of **real numbers**.

3) Describe **complex imaginary numbers**. How do they relate to fractional exponents and radicals? Give some examples.

Order of Operations

I. Review: How do the **first-level operations** of addition and subtraction produce the **second-level operations** of multiplication and division?

How does the **second-level operation** of multiplication produce the **third-level operation** of exponentiation?

II. Summarize the Order of Operation Rules for *evaluating* with the 3 levels of operations:

$+,\ -,\ \times,\ \div, \wedge, \sqrt{\ }$

III. Use the **Order of Operation rules** to evaluate each expression WITHOUT a calculator.

a) $36 \div 2^2 \times 3$

b) $3 \cdot \sqrt{32 - 7 + 11}$

c) $\frac{-28-3(2)^3}{5+8}$

d) $\frac{32+15\div(-3)}{2^4}$

e) $64 \div 8 \times \sqrt{25 - 9}$

f) $-7^2 - (20 - 14)^2$

g) $6(3 - 5)^3 - (4 - 1)^{-3}$

h) $\left(\frac{3}{4} + \frac{3}{5}\right)^2 + \sqrt[3]{-27}$

i) $-(-5)^0 - 3^0$

j) $\left(-\frac{1}{2}\right)^{-1}\left(-\frac{3}{4}\right) \div 1$

k) $16 + 8^{-\frac{4}{3}}$

l) $16 - 8^{\frac{4}{3}}$

m) $\left(-\frac{1}{2}\right)^{-1}\left(-\frac{3}{4}\right) \div 1$

n) $6 \times 4 \div 0$

o) $3 \div 9^{-\frac{1}{2}}$

p) $\left(-\frac{2}{3}(6-9)\right)^5$

q) $3\left(\frac{1}{6}-\frac{1}{4}\right)^2$

r) $-\frac{11}{8} \div \frac{1}{16} \times \frac{1}{-22} - \frac{8}{13}$

s) $\frac{60-2(3)^3}{\frac{6}{7}}$

t) $\left(-\frac{1}{2}\sqrt{10 \times 8 - 4^2}\right)^3$

0.3 Algebraic Expressions

I. Describe the difference between **terms** and **factors**. Give examples to illustrate.

Explain what it means if two **monomials**, or **terms** are **alike**. Give examples to illustrate.

II. For each **monomial**, simplify it, i.e., put it in **standard form**. Then identify its **coefficient** and its **degree**.

a) $3L(2L)^3$

coeff.:
degree:

b) $(5t)6t^2$

coeff.:
degree:

c) $(\frac{1}{2}W)(6W^3)(5W)$

coeff.:
degree:

d) $7r^2(5r)(2)$

coeff.:
degree:

e) $(5n)^2(2n)^3$

coeff.:
degree:

f) $3m^2(2m)^2$

coeff.:
degree:

III. Simplify each expression by using the distributive property when necessary and combining like terms.

a) $2L - 6 + 4L + 7L^3 + 8$

b) $2w - 6 + 4w + 5w^2 - (7w^2 + 8)$

c) $16p + 12p^2 - 4 - (-4p^2 - 10 + 4p)$

d) $-(22x - 3x + 4) + 6 - 5x$

e) $\frac{2}{3}p(30 + 19p^2)$

f) $9x(4 - 4x) + 4x^2 - 8x$

g) $15 - (2y - 7y^2) + 2y^2 - 3y$

h) $3t^2(5t - 6) + 4t^3$

i) $(3x - 2y)^2$

j) $(4w - 5)^2$

k) $(5b - 1)(2b + 7)$

l) $(10 - 4h)(7h + 1)$

IV. Evaluate each expression for the given values.

a) $x^2 - x + 1$ for $x = -3$

b) $\frac{-b+\sqrt{b^2-4ac}}{2a}$ for $a = -1, b = -2,$ and $c = 8$.

c) $-y^2 + 3y - 4$ for $y = -2$

d) $-4n^2 - n$ for $n = -5$

0.3 Intro to Algebraic Equations

I. What does the '=' symbol mean? How is it often misused? Give examples of correct and incorrect uses of it.

What is an **algebraic equation**? What is a **solution** to an algebraic equation? What does it mean to **solve** an equation?

II. Solve each equation by observation and reasoning. (Find all real solutions.) Be prepared to explain your answers.

a) $s^2 = 25$

b) $q^2 = -9$

c) $x = x + 1$

d) $3d + 2d = 5d$

Discuss the differences among the solutions to the equations above.

III. Describe a **linear equation**. Give examples and non-examples.

Describe a **power equation**. Give examples and non-examples.

IV. Simplify each **linear equation** and label it as a linear or as a power equation.
Then solve the equation algebraically by the balancing or by the mapping method. Show each step of your simplifying and solving process (even if you can do it in your head!)

1) $2s - 8 = -5s + 6$

2) $\frac{2}{3}(24x - 36) = 96$

3) $\frac{3}{5}(40v - 15) = 39$

4) $3h - \frac{5}{8} = \frac{3}{8}h + 2h$

5) $20 - (2x + 3) = 13 - 4x$

6) $10n + 5 = -\frac{7}{3} - 2n$

7) $3(4w + 6) + 8(12w - 9) = 38w + 58$

8) $12 - (14p + 6) = -(18 - 4p - 3)$

V. Simplify each **power equation** and label it as a linear or as a power equation.
Then solve the equation algebraically by the balancing or by the mapping method. Show each step of your simplifying and solving process (even if you can do it in your head!)

1) $430 = 0.8h^3$

2) $\frac{4}{5}A^2 = 2000$

3) $15r^2 + 5r^2 = 18{,}000$

4) $(5h)^2h = 20{,}000$

5). $20{,}850 = (2H)(8H)\left(\frac{1}{2}H\right)$

6). $39x^2 - 14x^2 = 62{,}5000$

7) $2n^3 + 6n^3 = 3065$

8) $-2t(2t^2) = -108$

9) $\left(\frac{4}{3}L^2\right)12L = 24{,}000$

10) $36b^2 - 22b^2 = 294$

VII. Simplify each equation and label it as a **linear** or as a **power** equation.
Then solve the equation algebraically by the balancing or by the mapping method. Show each step of your simplifying and solving process (even if you can do it in your head!)

1) $24(6t-7)+8(2t-6)=674$

2) $t^2+2t+1=t^2+20t-17$

3) $2d^3+d^3=0.024$

4) $(10L)(2.5L)=160{,}000$

5) $0.16=p(4p)$

6) $5x-10+3x=14-2x-10x+6$

7) $2y-10=48-(2y-1)$

8) $2x^2=-8$

9) $54000=-2V^3$

10) $342-(-20+14b-5)-6b=200$

11) $7500=65(2d-10)-20(4d+9)$

12) $\left(\frac{4}{3}W\right)(12W^2)=16{,}000$

0.4 Elementary Geometry: Shapes and Measures

0.4 Launch: Perimeter versus Area

What is the perimeter of a shape in the plane? What is the area of a shape in the plane? What is the difference between the two? Explain it in your own words. Work together with peers on the following tasks.

a) Draw *different* rectangles with areas of 24 square units. Label each with its perimeter. Which one has the smallest perimeter? Which has the largest?

b) Draw *different* rectangles with perimeters of 24 units. Label each with its area. Which one has the largest area? Which one has the smallest?

c) Discuss the units of measure for perimeter and area. Is it true that shapes with the same area must have the same perimeter? Or that if they have the same perimeter they must have the same area?

0.4 Angles, Triangles, and the Pythagorean Theorem

NOTE: When working with geometric figures, *always* draw and label a diagram!

I. Define a **circle**.

II. Find the angle that is the result of a rotation by the following fractions of a full circle.

a) $\frac{1}{10}$ b) $\frac{1}{6}$ c) $\frac{1}{2}$ d) $\frac{1}{4}$

Which of the angles above have special names? What are those names?

III. Describe in words each type of **triangle**. Draw and label diagrams to accompany your descriptions.

a) equilateral b) isosceles c) right

IV. State the **Pythagorean Theorem** by

a) writing an equation. b) drawing a labeled diagram.

c) explaining what it means in words.

V. For each problem, write any formulas used, draw and label a diagram, and then show how to answer the question algebraically. Round to hundredths.

a) The hypotenuse of a right triangle is 13 centimeters long and one of the legs is 4 cm long. Find the length of the other leg.

b) Find the leg length of an isosceles triangle if its base is 4 meters and the height (altitude) to its base is 5 meters.

c) How tall is a tree in the shape of an isosceles triangle with base 4 m and leg 5 m?

Tree: Malchev/Shutterstock.com

VI. What is a **diagonal**? Draw and label a diagram(s) to illustrate. Where do you come across diagonals in real life?

1) What is the diagonal across a rectangle with length 9 feet and width 3 feet? Round to hundredths.

2) What is the diagonal of a square with side length 1 foot?

0.4 Area

I. Define the **area** of a region. What kind of units are used to measure area?

II. Find the area of each figure below given that each segment on a grid represents 1 cm.

a) 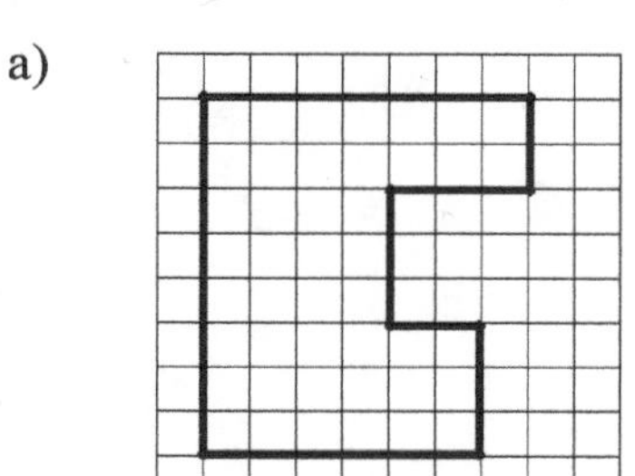

b) 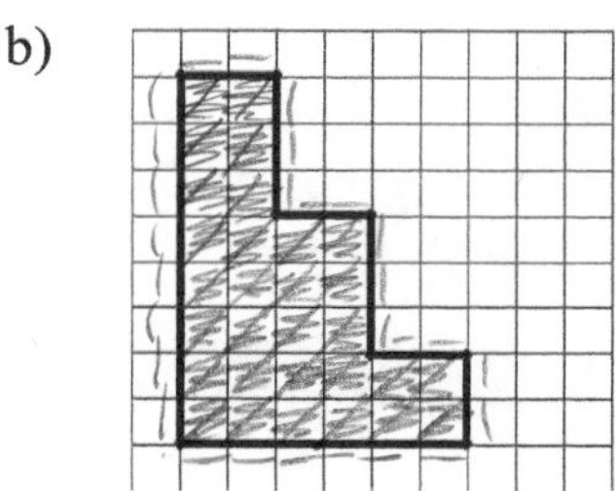

Area $30 cm^2$ ✓
perimeter 28 cm ✓

III. Write the area formulas for each shape. *As always*, draw and label diagrams to accompany formulas.

Area of a **rectangle**

Area of a **square**

Area of **parallelogram**

Area of a **triangle**

Area of a **circle**

IV. For each problem, write any formulas used, draw and label a diagram, and then show how to answer the question algebraically. Round to hundredths if rounding is necessary.

1) A rectangle has dimensions 6 inches by 2 feet. What is its area?

2) a. If a square has an *area* of 20 square meters, what is its side length?

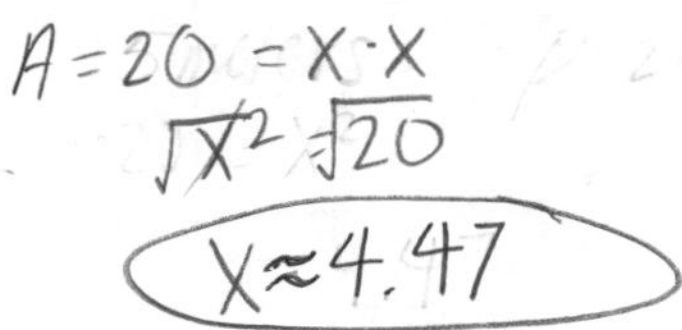

b. If a square has a *perimeter* of 20 meters, what is its side length?

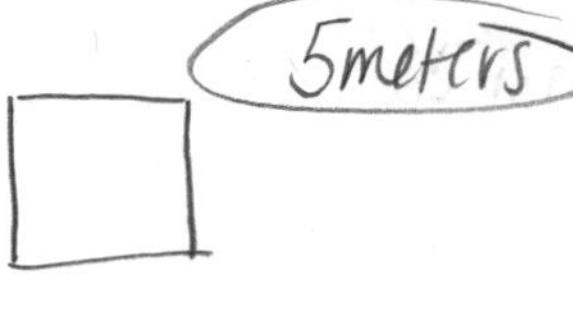

5meters

P = 20 = x+x+x+x

20/4 = 4x/4

X = 5

3) Calculate the area of a circle with a diameter of 17 yards.

4) Calculate the area of each triangle.

a)

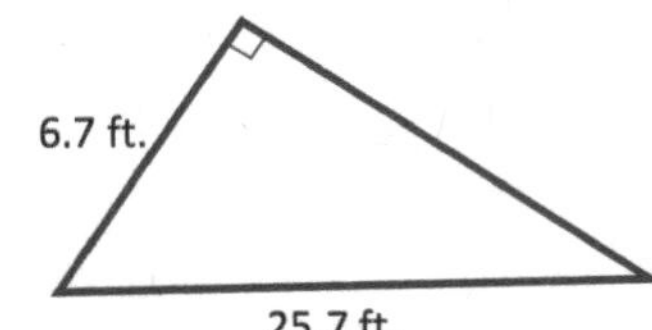

b)

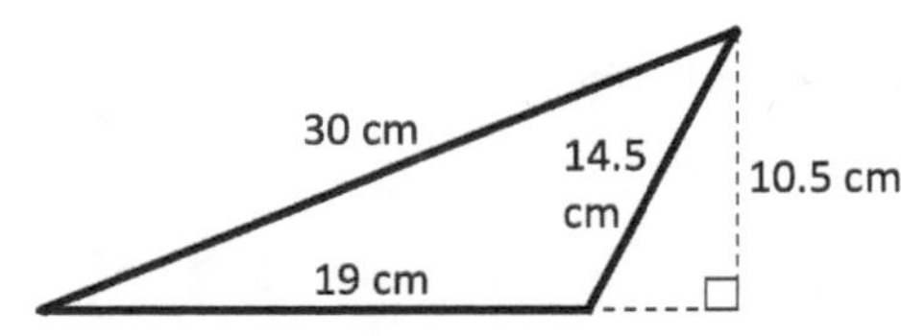

V. Name each figure. Then find its area where each line segment on a grid represents 1 meter. Show formulas used. Round to hundredths if rounding is necessary.

a)

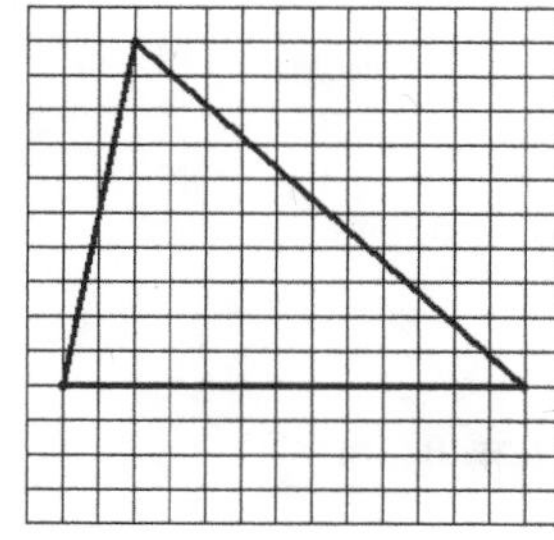

b)

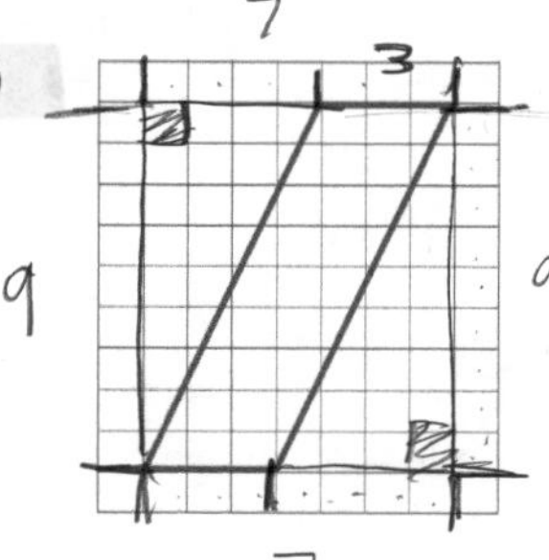

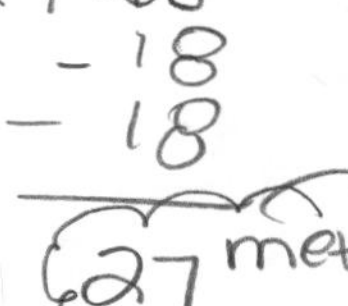

c)

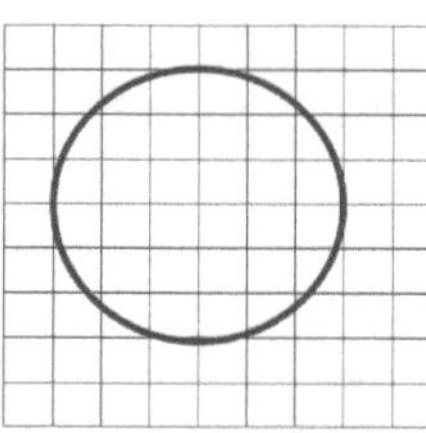

d)

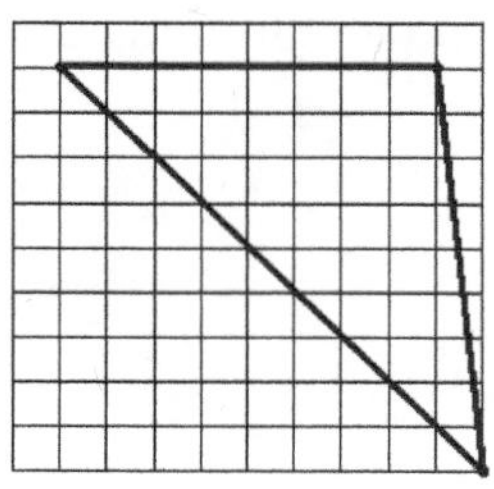

e)

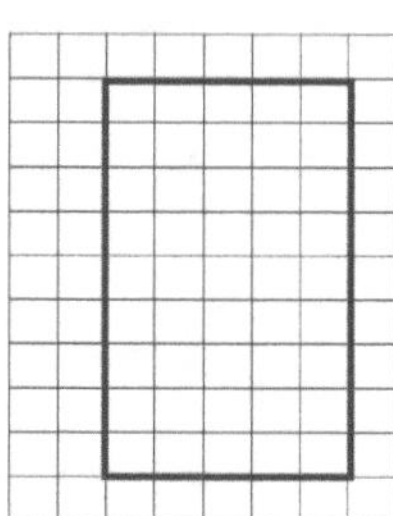

f)

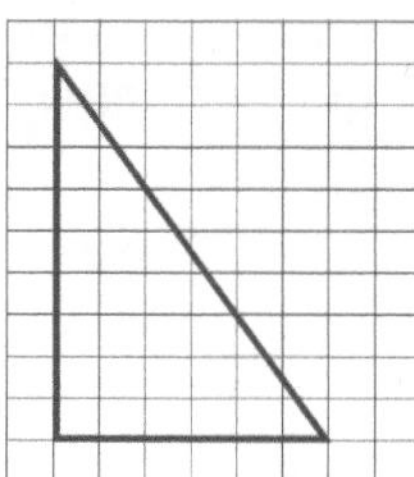

g)

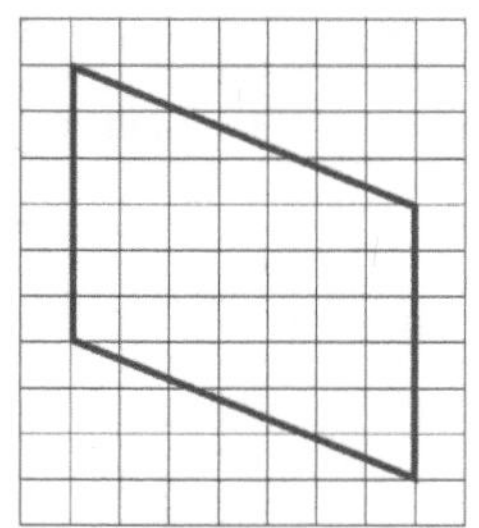

h)

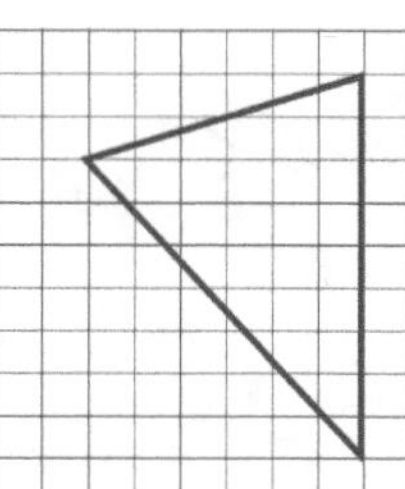

i)

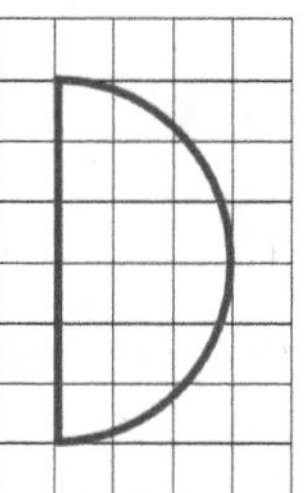

What is the formula for the area of this shape?

0.4 Perimeter

I. Define the **perimeter** of a region. What kind of units are used to measure perimeter?

II. Find the perimeter of each figure below given that each square on a grid represents 1 square cm.

a) 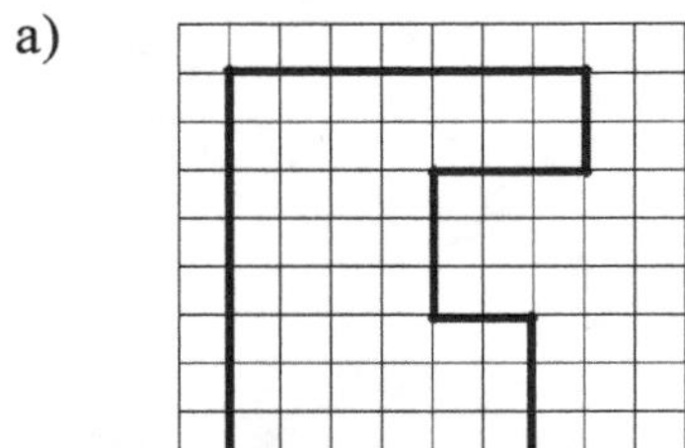

b) 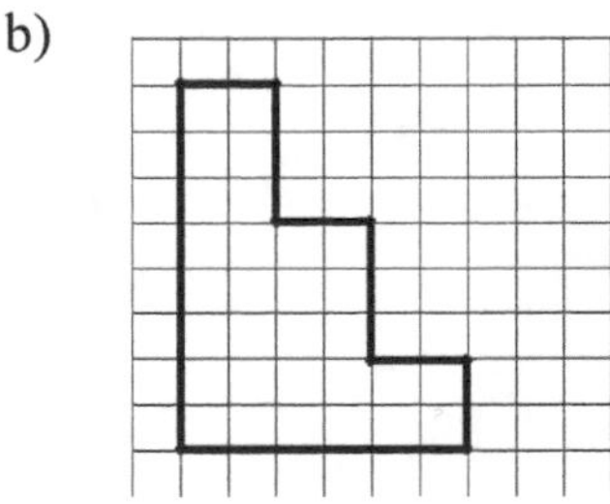

III. Write perimeter formulas for each shape. *As always*, draw and label diagrams to accompany formulas.
Perimeter of a **rectangle**

Perimeter of a **square**

Perimeter of **parallelogram**

Perimeter of a **triangle**

Perimeter of a **circle**

IV. For each problem, write any formulas used, draw and label a diagram, and then show how to answer the question algebraically. Round to hundredths if rounding is necessary.

1) A rectangle has dimensions 6 inches by 2 feet. What is its perimeter?

2) a. If a square has a *perimeter* of 64 meters, what is its side length?

b. If a square has an *area* of 64 square meters, what is its side length?

3) Calculate the perimeter of a circle with a diameter of 17 yards.

4) Calculate the perimeter of each figure.

a)

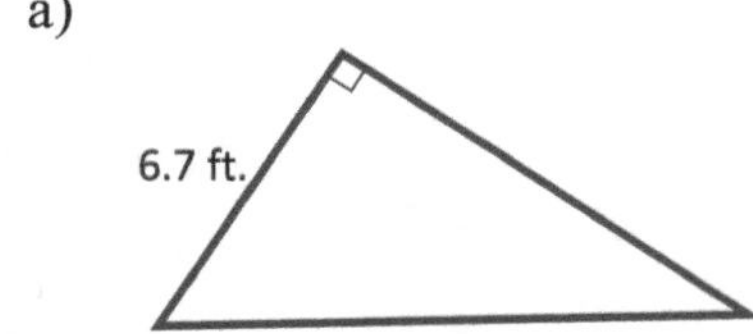

b)

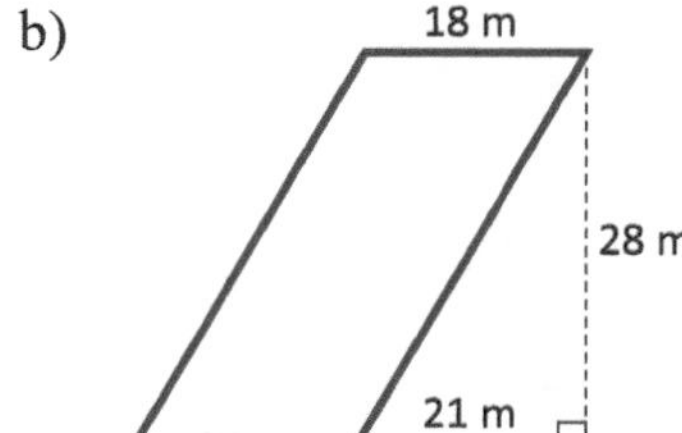

V. Name each figure and find its perimeter where each square on a grid represents 1 square inch. Show formulas. Round to hundredths if rounding is necessary.

a) 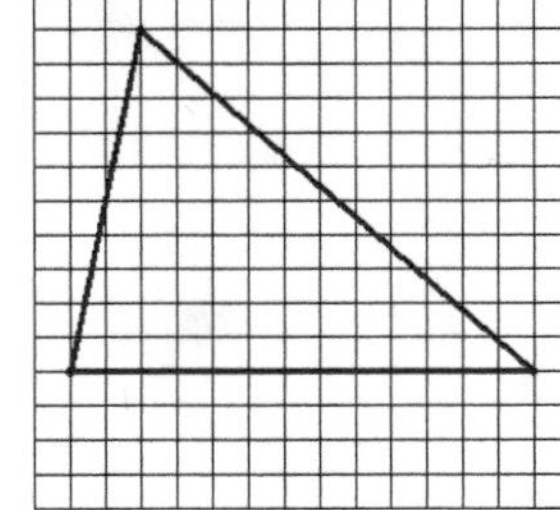

b) 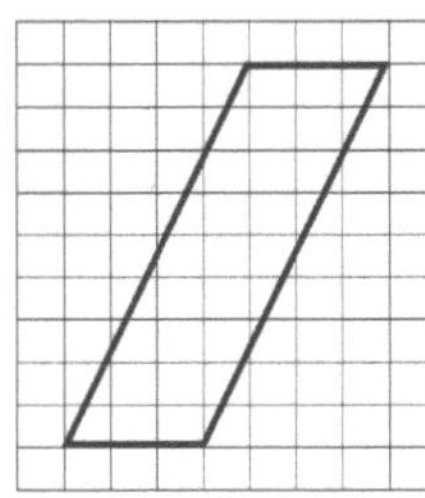

c) 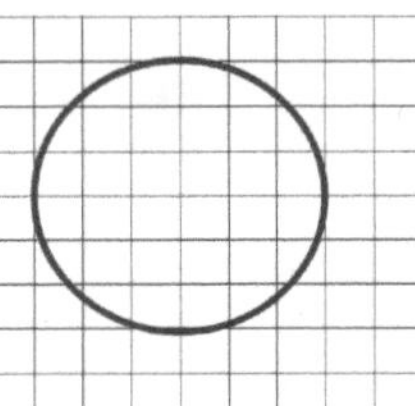

d) 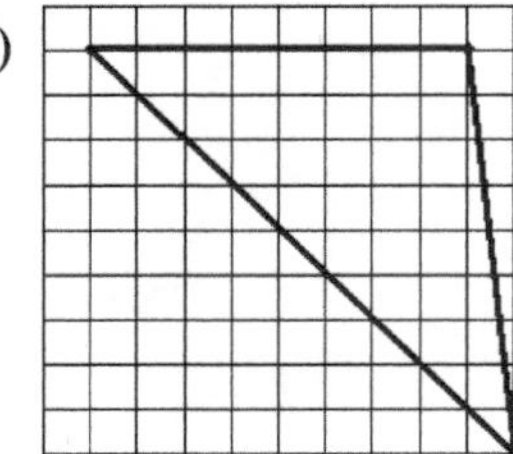

e) 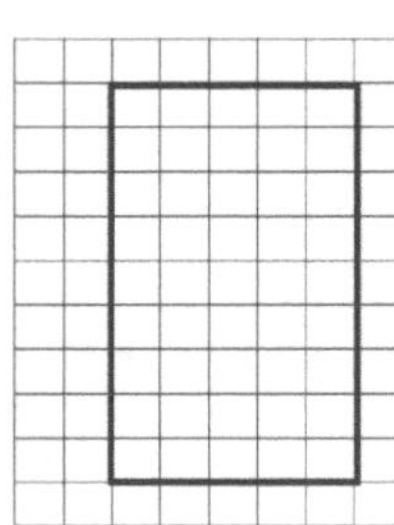

f) 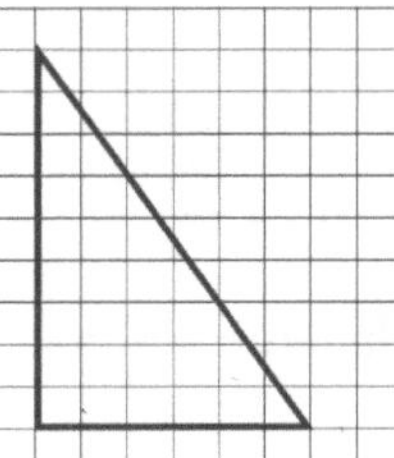

g) 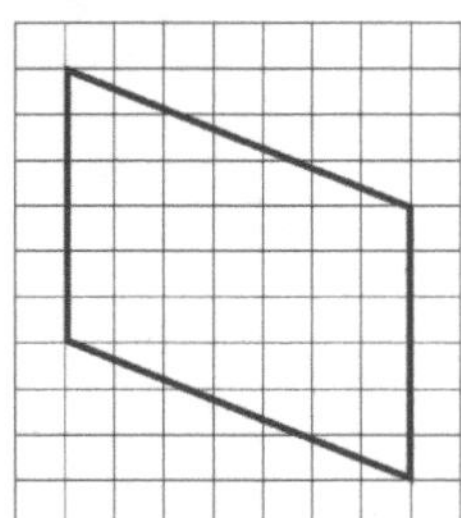

h) 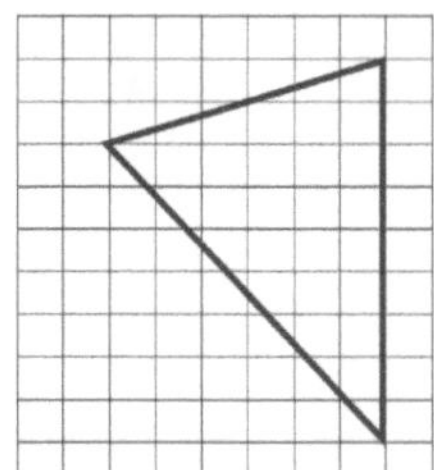

i) 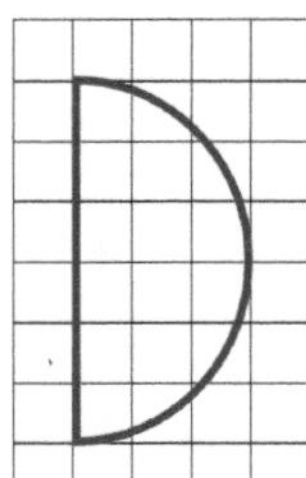

What is the formula for the perimeter of this shape?

0.4 Area and Perimeter Mixed Practice

I. For each figure,

- Write formulas for the perimeter and for the area.
- Draw and label diagrams with numerical values or with variables in the formulas.
- Evaluate the formulas to find the perimeter and the area. Label answers with units.

1) Perimeter:

1)

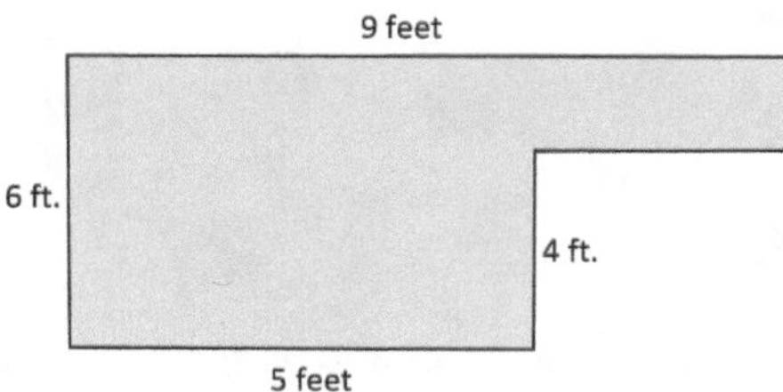

Area:

2) Perimeter:

2)

1 in.

Area:

3) Perimeter:

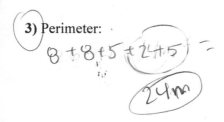

3)

1 m

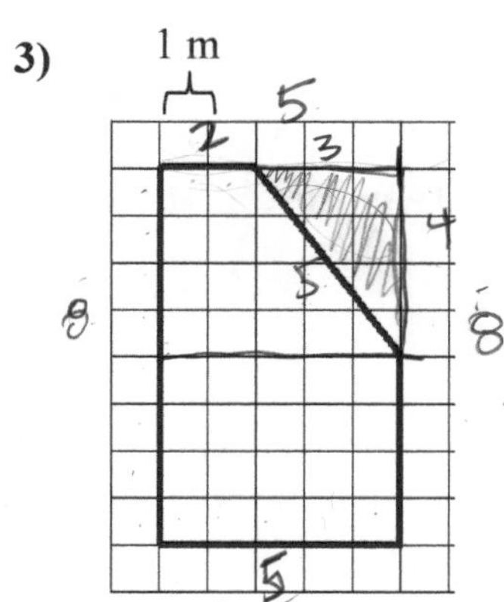

Area:

4) *A circle with diameter 35 feet.*

Perimeter:

Area:

0.4 Critical Thinking

I. Answer TRUE or FALSE. If TRUE, explain why it is true. If FALSE, give an example to verify it is false.

1) Given two rectangles, the rectangle with a larger perimeter will always have a larger area.

2) Given two rectangles, the rectangle with a larger area will always have a larger perimeter.

II. What is the sum of the interior angles of any triangle?

1) What are the interior angles of an equilateral triangle?

2) What are the interior angles of an isosceles right triangle?

3) An isosceles triangle has one interior angle of 120 degrees. What are the other two angles?

4) An isosceles triangle has one interior angle of 70 degrees. What are the other two angles?

0.4 Volume

I. For each 3-dimensional solid below, the shaded 2-dimensional faces are called **bases**.

name of base:				
name of solid:				
# faces				
# sides				
# vertices				

II. Name the 3-dimensional solids below and their bases.

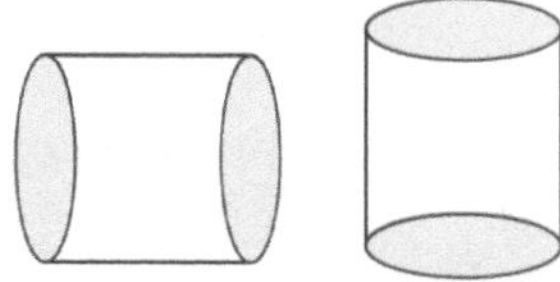

III. Define the **volume** of a solid. What kind of units are used to measure volume?

IV. Find the volume of the right prism whose base is the figure on the grid where each square is 1 square unit and the extended distance is 7 units. Name the unit of the volume.

a)

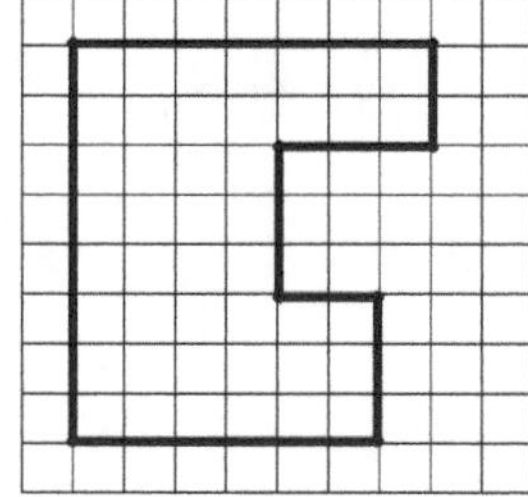

Volume with unit:

b)

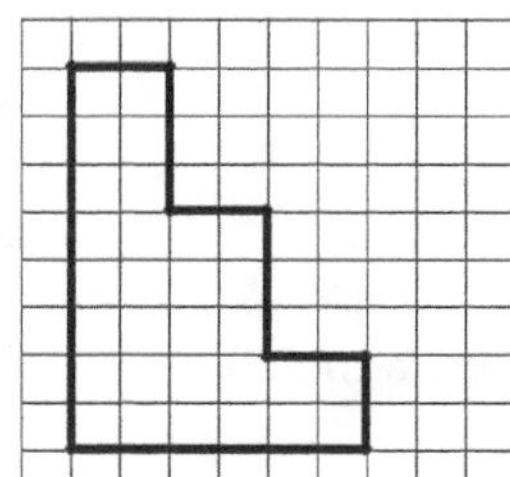

Volume with unit:

V. Write volume formulas for each solid. *As always*, label diagrams to accompany formulas.

Volume of a **right rectangular prism**

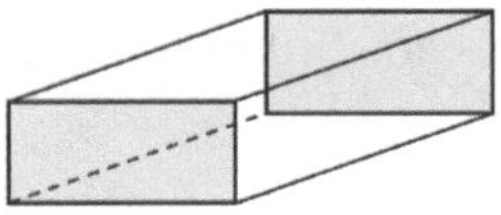

Volume of a **cube**

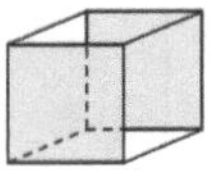

Volume of a **right triangular prism**

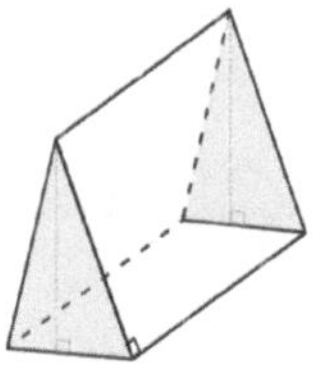

Volume of a **right cylinder**

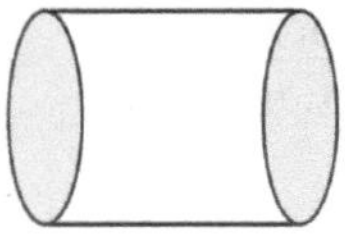

VI. For each solid, write the volume formula, draw and label a diagram, and evaluate the formula to find the volume.

1) A shipping container has the shape of a box with a length of 5 meters and a rectangular base with dimensions 3 meters by 4 meters.

2) A tent has the shape of a right triangular prism. Its length is 2.4 meters, its height is 1.6 meters, and the width of the triangular end is 2.4 meters.

3) A box with dimensions 6 inches by 2 feet by 13 inches.

4) A cube with side length 5 centimeters.

5) A glass in the shape of a right cylinder with diameter 7.24 cm and height 9 cm.

6) A shipping box in the shape of a right triangular prism. The triangular base has an area of 38 square inches and the box has length 2 feet.

7) A tanker in the shape of a right cylinder with length 20 feet and radius 2.5 feet.

VII. For each solid, write the volume formula and then evaluate it to find the volume. Label answers with units.

1)

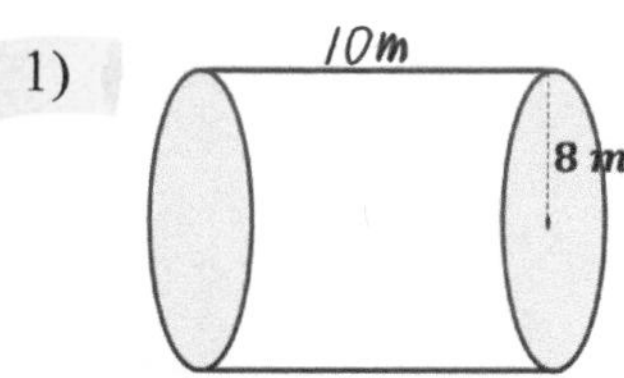

Volume formula: Ao × d

$\pi r^2 \cdot d$

2009.6 m3

2)

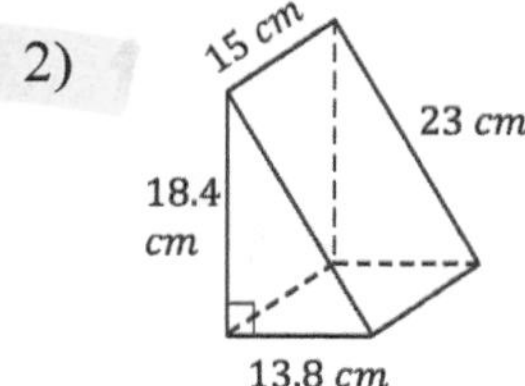

Volume formula: $\frac{1}{2} b \cdot h \times d$

126.96
× 15

1904.4 cm3

3)

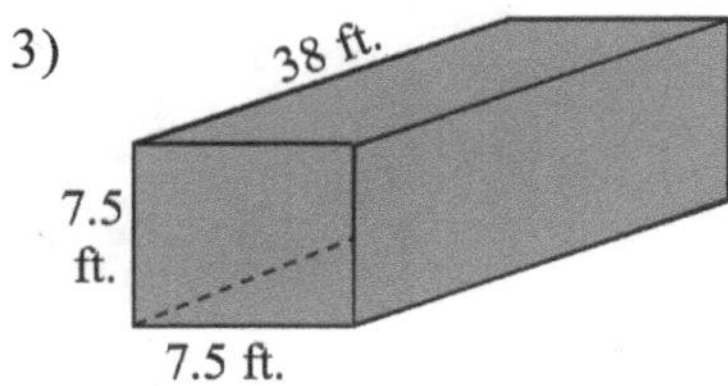

Volume formula:

4)

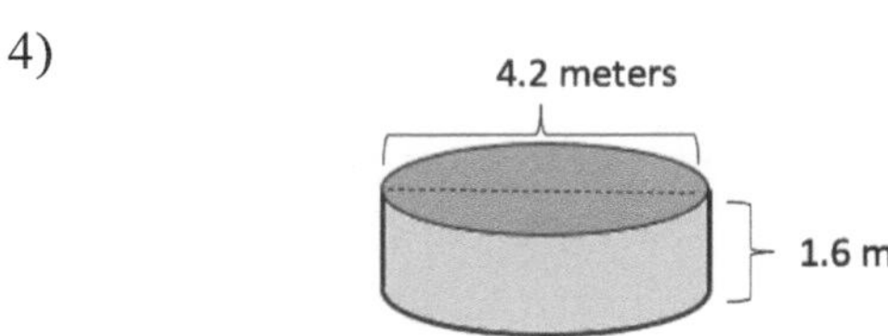

Volume formula:

5)

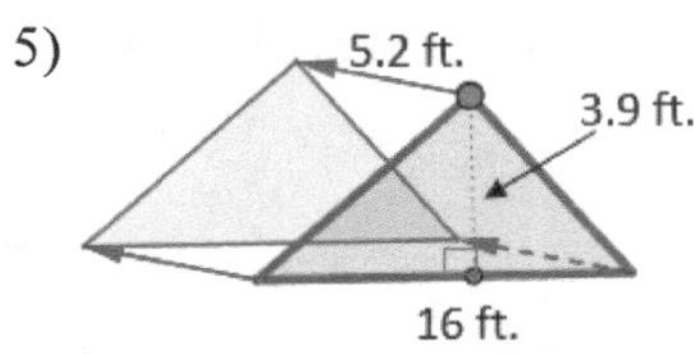

Volume formula:

6)

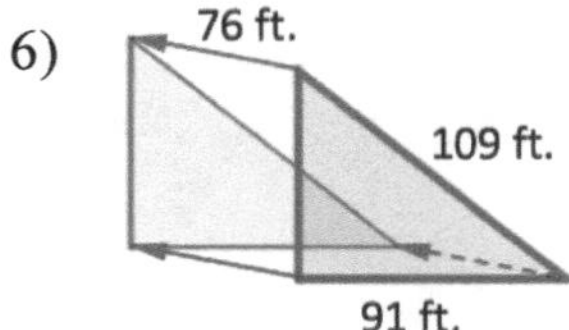

Volume formula:

7)

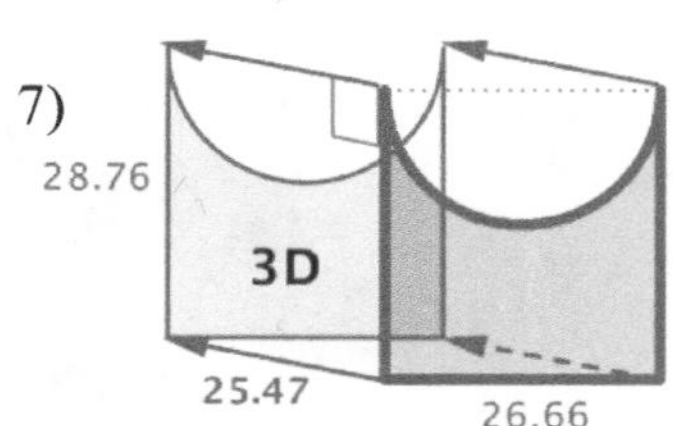

Volume formula:
(create one)

Self-Assessment Test 0: Elementary Arithmetic, Algebra, and Geometry

Instructions: Part ONE is to be completed WITHOUT a CALCULATOR.
For full credit, you must show how you did all of your calculations.

1) Write each number in decimal form:

a) *Sixty Trillion, Five Hundred Thirty-two Million, Seven Thousand, Three Hundred one*

b) *Twenty and sixty-four Ten-Thousandths*

2) Round the number 750,985.0855 to each of the following levels of rounding.

a) millions

b) hundreds

c) tens

d) tenths

e) hundredths

f) thousandths

3) Use standard algorithms to perform each operation.

a) 37×849

b) $7083 - 684$

c) $40{,}107 \div 87$

4) a. What is a prime number?

b. Give the prime factorization of 1050.

5) Name the fraction (NOT a mixed number) represented by the entire shaded region if the whole is TWO of the long bars (rectangles) in the figure at right.

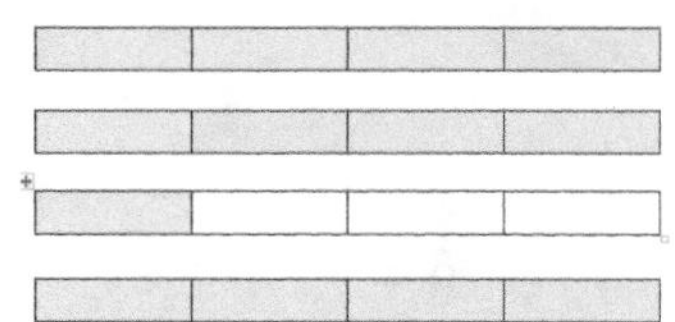

6) Write an example of an undefined fraction.

7) Draw appropriate tick marks and use them to show the location of $\frac{10}{3}$ on the number line. Place a dot at the location of $\frac{10}{3}$ and show the dot with an arrow.

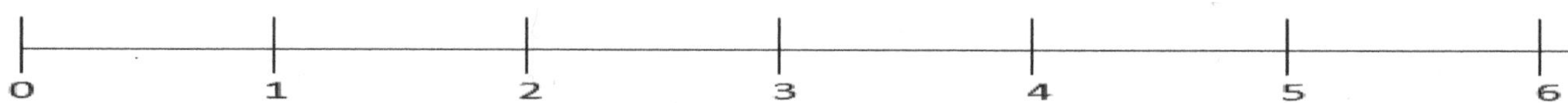

8) Determine which fraction is greater: $\frac{7}{15}$, $\frac{18}{35}$. You must justify your answer for credit using a common denominator, a common numerator, or a benchmark fraction.

9) Convert each fraction into decimal form AND into a percentage. Show work with equivalent fractions.

a) $\frac{3}{20}$

b) $\frac{9}{75}$

10) Convert each decimal number into an ordinary fraction (proper or improper) AND to a percentage.

a) 0.057

b) 3.08

11) Convert each percentage to an ordinary fraction (proper or improper) AND to a decimal form.

a) 4.9%

b) 345%

12) Evaluate each expression and show work when appropriate. The answer must be an integer, a fraction, undefined, or a complex imaginary number.

a) $\frac{4}{10} - \frac{11}{15} \times 5$

b) $3.8 - \frac{3}{5}$

c) $\sqrt[3]{5^2 + 2}$

d) $8 \div \frac{3}{4}$

e) $12 \div 0 \times 6$

f) $\frac{1}{3} \div 6 \times 3$

g) $40 - 10 + 12 \div 3 \times 2$

h) $36 \div 2^2 \times 3$

i) $200 - (8 + 2)^2$

j) $32^{\frac{2}{5}}$

k) $\sqrt{4 - 20}$

l) $-3^2 \times 5^{-2}$

m) $\frac{18-(24-10+4)}{-3^2}$

n) $\frac{7}{9} \div \frac{5}{3} - 1$

o) $36 \div \left(\frac{3}{2}\right)^{-1}$

13) Recall the Interpretations of Multiplication, $\boldsymbol{M} \times \boldsymbol{N} = \boldsymbol{P}$, and Division $\boldsymbol{P} \div \boldsymbol{N} = \boldsymbol{M}$, or $\boldsymbol{P} \div \boldsymbol{M} = \boldsymbol{N}$ where

$\boldsymbol{M}$ = abstract **M**ultiplier (the number of wholes)
$\boldsymbol{N}$ = concrete **N**umber (the number of units per whole)
$\boldsymbol{P}$ = concrete **P**roduct (the total number of units)

For each problem, perform a unit analysis and write an equation of one of the forms above to answer the question. You can evaluate (a) using stepwise multiplication and division by integers, or (b) using fraction multiplication/division.

a) *Today we ate* $\frac{3}{5}$ *of the* $\frac{2}{3}$ *pan of brownies left from yesterday. How much did we eat today?*

Concrete unit: Equation: Answer:

b) *There was* $\frac{7}{8}$ *of a pan of brownies leftover. If we share it equally among 5 friends, how much does each get?*

Concrete unit: Equation: Answer:

c) *There was* $\frac{4}{5}$ *of a pan of brownies left over. If it is split up so that each friend gets* $\frac{1}{10}$ *of a pan, how many friends get* $\frac{1}{10}$ *of a pan?*

Concrete unit: Equation: Answer:

<u>**Instructions**</u>**: Part TWO is to be completed with a CALCULATOR ALLOWED.**
For full credit, you must show how you did all of your calculations. Label ALL answers with units.
Do NOT round in your calculations. Round final answers to the nearest hundredth if rounding is necessary.

14) For each problem,

- Draw and label a double or triple number line model. Mark the origin, the given ratio, and the unknown.
- Write a proportion to represent the problem.
- Solve the proportion algebraically with cross multiplication or equivalent fraction simplification or amplification.

a) *At a farm, the ratio of cows to pigs is 7 to 5. If there are 840 cows and pigs altogether, how many are cows?*

Number lines:

Proportion:

b) *A student has read 378 pages of a book. If this is 30% of the book, how many pages are in the whole book?*

Number lines:

Proportion:

15) Simplify each expression.

a) $3t(5t)^2$

b) $(3w)7w^2$

c) $(\frac{1}{2}L)(6L^2)(8L)$

d) $8x + 2x^2 - 4 - (-49 - 32x^2 + 4x)$

e) $7w - 12 + 2w + 54 - (10w^2 + 1)$

16) Solve each equation algebraically. Simplify and show all the steps in the balancing method.

a) $41 - (12p - 11) = -(18 - 17p - 41)$

b) $\left(\frac{3}{4}L^2\right)8L = 3{,}000$

c) $22b^2 - 7b^2 = 9630$

d) $982 - (-20 + 14b - 5) - 6b = 260$

For full credit on the following problems, you must label answers with units.

17) a) Find the missing side length of the triangle shown at right.

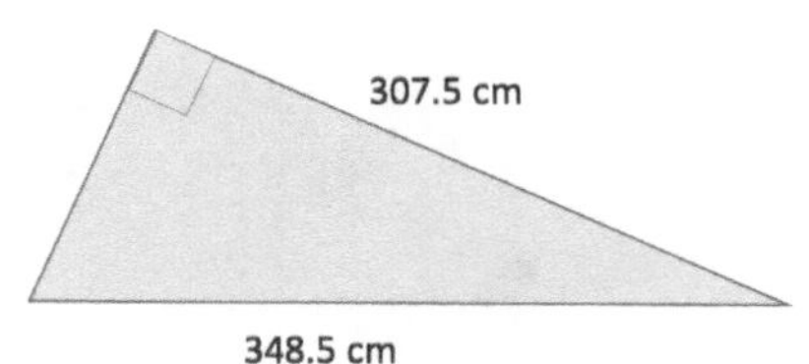

b) Find the area of the same triangle. Show ALL work and label your answer with the unit.

18) a) Find the radius of the semicircle at right.

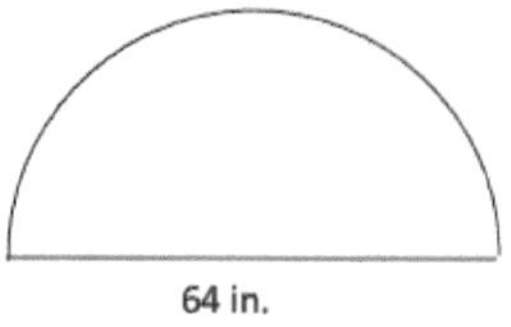

64 in.

b) Calculate the *perimeter* of the semicircle. Write a formula and show work.

Formula:

c) Calculate the *area* of the semicircle. Write a formula and show work.

Formula:

19) Find the volume for each solid shown below. Write the formulas you use and show work.

a)

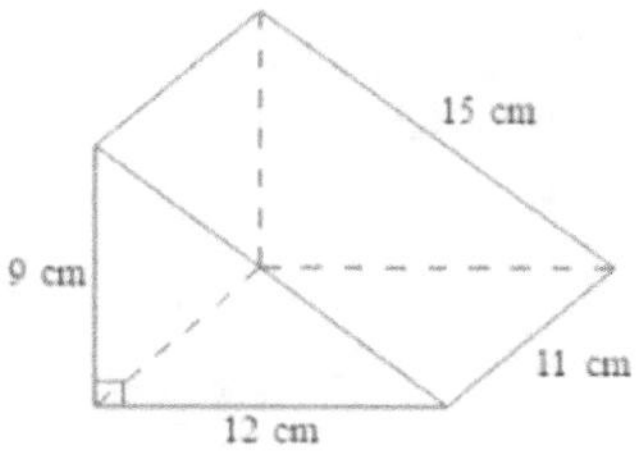

15 cm
9 cm
11 cm
12 cm

b)

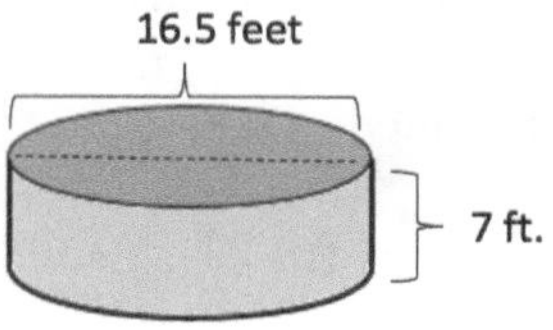

16.5 feet
7 ft.

c)

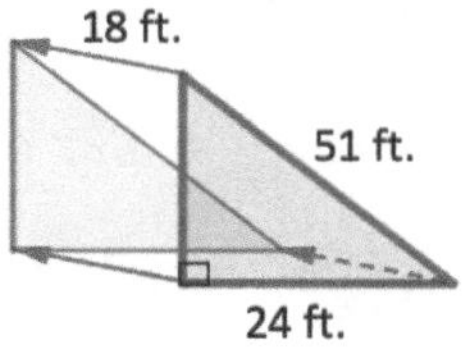

18 ft.
51 ft.
24 ft.

a) Formula:

b) Formula:

c) Formula:

Answer Key: Test 0

1) (a) 60,000,532,007,301; (b) 20.0064

2) (a) 1,000,000; (b) 751,000; (c) 750,990; (d) 750,985.1; (e) 750,985.09; (f) 750,985.086

3) (a) 31,413; (b) 6399; (c) 461

4) (a) A number is prime if it has exactly two natural divisors.; (b) $1050 = 2 \cdot 3 \cdot 5 \cdot 5 \cdot 7$

5) $\frac{13}{8}$ 6) $\frac{5}{0}$ is undefined – any fraction with a zero denominator

7) $\frac{10}{3}$:

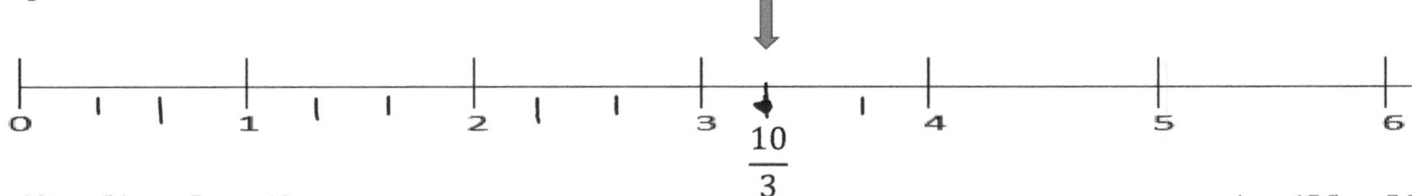

8) $\frac{18}{35} = \frac{54}{105} > \frac{7}{15} = \frac{49}{105}$ by common denominator or by comparing both to a benchmark of $\frac{1}{2} = \frac{17.5}{35} = \frac{7.5}{15}$.

9) (a) $\frac{3}{20} = \frac{15}{100} = 0.15 = 15\%$; (b) $\frac{9}{75} = \frac{3}{25} = \frac{12}{100} = 12\% = 0.12$

10) (a) $0.0057 = \frac{57}{10{,}000} \frac{\div 100}{\div 100} = \frac{0.57}{100} = 0.57\%$; (b) $3.08 = \frac{308}{100} = \frac{77}{25} = 308\%$

11) (a) $4.9\% = \frac{4.9}{100} \frac{\times 10}{\times 10} = \frac{49}{1000} = 0.049$; (b) $345\% = \frac{345}{100} = 3.45$

12) (a) $-\frac{49}{15}$; (b) $\frac{16}{5} = 3.2$; (c) 3; (d) $\frac{32}{3}$; (e) undefined; (f) $\frac{1}{6}$; (g) 38; (h) 27; (i) 100; (j) 4;

(k) imaginary complex; (l) $-\frac{9}{25}$; (m) 0; (n) $-\frac{8}{15}$; (o) 24

13) (a) concrete unit: pan of brownies; $\frac{3}{5} \times \frac{2}{3} = \frac{6}{15} = \frac{2}{5}$; we ate $\frac{2}{5}$ pan

(b) concrete unit: pan of brownies; $\frac{7}{8} \div 5 = \frac{7}{8} \times \frac{1}{5} = \frac{7}{40}$; each person gets $\frac{7}{40}$ of a pan

(c) concrete unit: pan of brownies; $\frac{4}{5} \div \frac{1}{10} = \frac{4}{5} \times \frac{10}{1} = \frac{40}{5} = 8$; 8 friends

14) (a) $\frac{cows}{pigs} \frac{7}{5} \Rightarrow \frac{cows}{total} \frac{7}{12} = \frac{c}{840}$; $c = 490$ cows; (b) $\frac{pages}{percent} \frac{378}{30} = \frac{p}{100} \Rightarrow p = 1260$ pages

15) (a) $75t^3$; (b) $21w^3$; (c) $24L^4$; (d) $34x^2 + 4x + 45$; (e) $-10w^2 + 9w + 41$

16) (a) $p = 1$; (b) $L = \sqrt[3]{500} \approx 7.94$; (c) $b = \pm\sqrt{642} \approx \pm 25.34$; (d) $b = \frac{747}{20} = 37.35$

17) (a) missing side length $\sqrt{26{,}896} = 164$ cm; (b) $A_\Delta = \frac{1}{2}bh = \frac{1}{2}(307.5)(164) = 9{,}840$ sq. cm

18) (a) radius = 32 inches; (b) $P_{semicircle} = \frac{C}{2} + d = \frac{2\pi r}{2} + d = \pi r + d = \pi(32) + 64 \approx 164.48\ inches$

(c) $A_{semicircle} = \frac{1}{2}\pi r^2 = \frac{1}{2}\pi(32)^2 \approx 1{,}607.68\ square\ inches$

19) (a) $V_{triangular\ prism} = \frac{1}{2}bhd = \frac{1}{2}(9)(12)(11) = 594$ cubic cm

(b) $V_{cylinder} = \pi r^2 h = \pi(8.25)^2 \approx 213.72$ cubic feet

(c) $V_{triangular\ prism} = \frac{1}{2}bhd = \frac{1}{2}(24)(45)(18) = 9{,}720$ cubic feet, where 45 ft. is the missing leg

Unit 1 Quantitative Analysis, Problem Solving, and Functions

1.1 Quantitative Analysis

1.1 Launch: Shopping Trip

Last week you bought shirts, jeans, and notebooks. The shirts cost $15 each, the jeans cost $30 each, and each notebook costs $5. You must consider the total cost of the items.

Which quantities are *given* or *known* in this situation? We call these **constants**.

numerical value	unit of measure	detailed description of the quantity

Which quantities are *not explicitly given* or are *unknown*? We call these **variables**.

smart label	unit of measure	detailed description of the quantity	discrete or continuous

c) [Section 1.2 - Algebraic Relations] *Assume the number of jeans purchased is 3 less than the number of shirts bought, and the number of notebooks purchased is 2 more than the number of shirts.* Translate these requirements into symbolic language using your labels above. Write any other formula(s) that relate the quantities in this situation.

d) [Section 1.3 – Problem Solving] *Assume the total amount spent on the items was $175.* Solve algebraically for the number of each item purchased.

1.1 Launch: Fencing a Pen

Simone is going to fence in a rectangular pen in the yard where her dog can play. The area of the pen will be 228 square feet. To buy materials, Simone must consider the length, width, and perimeter of the pen.

Which quantities are *given* or *known* in this situation? (**constants**)

numerical value	unit of measure	detailed description of the quantity

Which quantities are *not explicitly given* or are *unknown*? (**variables**) Draw and label a diagram.

smart label	unit of measure	detailed description of the quantity	discrete/ continuous

Labeled Diagram:

c) [Section 1.2 - Algebraic Relations] *Assume the width of the pen is 17.75 feet less than twice its length.* Translate that requirement into symbolic language using your labels above. Write any other formula(s) that relate the quantities in this situation.

d) [Section 1.3A – Problem Solving] Solve algebraically for the dimensions and for the perimeter of the pen.

1.1 Problems

1. *A company makes semicircular windows. The catalog lists 138.78 inches of trim around all the edges of a window but does not list its area.*

a) Which quantities are *given* or *known* in this situation? **(constants)**

numerical value	unit of measure	detailed description of the quantity

b) Which quantities are *not explicitly given* or are *unknown*? **(variables)** Draw and label a diagram.

smart label	unit of measure	detailed description of the quantity	discrete/ continuous

<u>Labeled Diagram:</u>

c) [Section 1.2 - Algebraic Relations] Write the formulas that relate the quantities in this situation.

d) [Section 1.3A – Problem Solving] Solve algebraically for the dimensions and for the perimeter of the pen.

2. *We are going to build a bookcase like the one shown at right where its width and height are measured in centimeters. The total length of board needed to cut the shelves and sides, including the top and bottom, is exactly 6.63 meters. We will also want to know the area of the board for the back.*

a) Which quantities are given or known in this situation? (**constants**)

numerical value	unit of measure	detailed description of the quantity
6.63	meters	total length of board needed to cut

cm 6.63 m

b) Which quantities are not explicitly given or unknown? (**variables**) Label the diagram with variables.

smart label	unit of measure	detailed description of the quantity	discrete/ continuous
A	m^2	AREA of Board	continuous
H	cm	Height	continuous
W	cm	width	continuous

c) [Section 1.2 - Algebraic Relations] Assume the height of the bookcase is 6 cm less than twice its width, and we want the width of the shelves to be more than 60cm each to fit our books. Translate the requirements into symbolic language using your labels above. Write any other formula(s) that relate the quantities in this situation.

d) [Section 1.3A – Problem Solving] Solve for the dimensions and area of the bookcase algebraically. Then verify the constraint given by the inequality.

3. *The base of carton (right prism) is a right triangle whose longer leg is 3 times its shorter leg. The depth of the carton is three fourths of the shorter leg. The volume of the carton is less than 800 cubic inches and more than 500 cubic inches.*

a) Which quantities are *given* or *known* in this situation? **(constants)**

numerical value	unit of measure	detailed description of the quantity

b) Which quantities are *not explicitly given* or are *unknown*? **(variables)** Draw and label a diagram. Labeled Diagram:

smart label	unit of measure	detailed description of the quantity	discrete/ continuous

c) [Section 1.2 - Algebraic Relations] Translate the requirements into symbolic language. Write any other formula(s) that relate the quantities in (a)-(b).

d) [Section 1.3B – Problem Solving] *Assume the volume of the pool is 576 cubic feet. How deep is the pool?* Solve for the dimensions of the carton algebraically. Then verify the constraints given by the inequalities.

4. *A customer bought 2 frozen dinners, 3 identical drinks, and a pack of gum. One frozen dinner costs $1.25 less than triple the cost of a drink. The pack of gum costs $1.30 more than a drink. The total cost for all of the items was $23.70, and we want to know the price of each item.*

a) Which quantities are *given* or *known* in this situation? (**constants**)

numerical value	unit of measure	detailed description of the quantity

b) Which quantities are *not explicitly given* or are *unknown*? (**variables**)

smart label	unit of measure	detailed description of the quantity	discrete/ continuous

c) [Section 1.2 - Algebraic Relations] Translate the requirements into symbolic language. Write any other formula(s) that relate the quantities in (a)-(b).

d) [Section 1.3A – Problem Solving] Solve for the prices of each item algebraically.

1.1 Concepts and Vocabulary

1. Explain the meaning of each term in your own words. Give examples.

a) Quantity

b) Unit of measure

c) Variable

d) Constant

e) Continuous variable

f) Discrete variable

1.2 Algebraic Relations

1.2 Launch: Building a Patio

Suppose we are building a rectangular patio. We have only enough pavers for 300 square feet, and we plan to use exactly 912 inches of trim for the edges. We also want the width of the patio to be one foot less than half its length.

a) Perform the quantitative analysis. [This part can be completed in section 1.1.]

Constants

numerical value	unit of measure	detailed description of the quantity

Variables

smart label	unit of measure	detailed description of the quantity	discrete/ continuous

Labeled Diagram:

b) Translate the requirements into symbolic language using your labels above. Write any other formula(s) that relate the quantities in this situation.

c) [Section 1.3A – Problem Solving] Can we build a patio satisfying all of the requirements?

1.2 Problems

1. *Abe, Bella, and Carlos all have earned college credits. ~~Bella has earned 17 credits more than Abe,~~ and Carlos has earned 9 less than triple the number of Abe's credits. Together they have a total of 183 credits. How many credits has each earned?*

a) Which quantities are *given* or *known* in this situation? **(constants)**

value	unit	detailed description of the quantity
T	183 credits	TOTal credits of all students ✓

b) Which quantities are *not explicitly given* or are *unknown*? **(variables)**

label	unit	detailed description of the quantity	disc./cont.
B	credits	Bellas credits	discreet
A	credits	Abe's credits	discreet
C	credits	Carlos credits	discreet

b) Translate requirements into symbolic language. Write any other formula(s) that relate the quantities.

$B = A + 17$

$C = 3A - 9$

$A + B + C = 183$

c) [Section 1.3A – Problem Solving] Solve for the number of each students' credits algebraically.

$$\begin{cases} B = A + 17 \\ C = 3a - 9 \\ A + B + C = 183 \end{cases}$$

$35 + 17 = 52 = B$

$C = 96$

$A + A + 17 + 3a - 9 = 183$

$5A + 17 - 9 = 183$

$5a + 8 = 183$

$-8 \quad -8$

$5a = 175$

$/5 \quad /5$

$A = 35$

2. *Exactly 58 feet of trim goes around the edge of an office, not including the 48-inch doorway, as shown in the diagram. The width of the office is 8 feet shorter than its length. We need to know the area of the office floor to buy a new carpet.*

a) Perform the quantitative analysis including labeling the diagram. [This part can be completed in section 1.1.]

Constants

value	unit	detailed description of the quantity

Desk: benchmark/Shutterstock.com

Variables

label	unit	detailed description of the quantity	disc./cont.

b) Translate the requirements into symbolic language using your labels above. Write any other formula(s) that relate the quantities in this situation.

c) [Section 1.3A – Problem Solving] Solve algebraically for the area of the floor.

3. *A van is loaded 24 laptops, 7 television sets (TVs), and 16 printers. The weight of one laptop is 13.5 pounds less than one printer, and one TV set weighs 19 pounds more than one printer. The total weight of the items in the van is 843 pounds. We want to know the weight of each item the van is carrying.*

a) Perform the quantitative analysis. [This part can be completed in section 1.1.]

value	unit	detailed description of the **constant** quantity
24	~~laptop~~	Laptops in van
7	TV	TVs in van
16	~~printer~~	printers in van
843	pounds	total weight

label	unit	detailed description of the **variable** quantity	disc/cont.
L	pounds	weight of a laptop	cont.
T	pounds	tv weights of a printer	Cont.

b) Translate requirements into symbolic language. Write any other formula(s) that relate the quantities.

$L = P - 13.5$

$T = 19 + P$

c) [Section 1.3A – Problem Solving] Solve for the weight of each item algebraically.

4. *A cylindrical container has a capacity of 539 cubic inches. Its radius is one fifth of its height. To buy the correct sized lid, we need to find the diameter of the top.*

a) Perform the quantitative analysis including labeling the diagram. [This part can be completed in section 1.1.]

value	unit	detailed description of the **constant** quantity
539	cubic inches	Cylindrical container volume

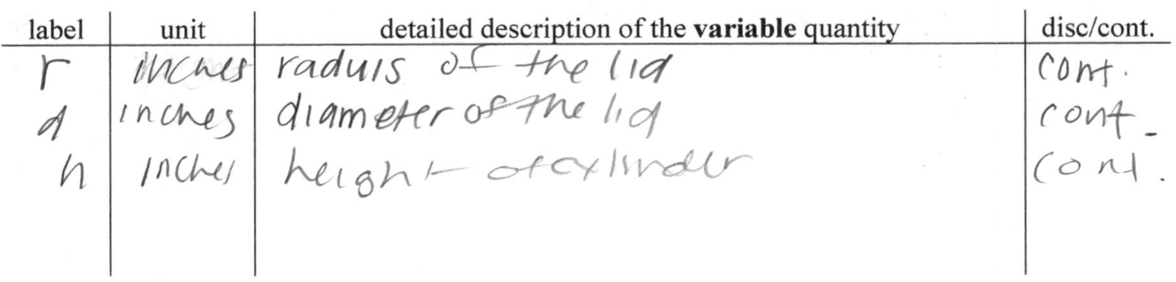

label	unit	detailed description of the **variable** quantity	disc/cont.
r	inches	radius of the lid	cont.
d	inches	diameter of the lid	cont.
h	inches	height of cylinder	cont.

b) Translate requirements into symbolic language. Write any other formula(s) that relate the quantities.

$539 = 3.14 r^2 h$

$V = \frac{1}{5} h$

c) [Section 1.3 – Problem Solving] Solve algebraically for the diameter of the container. Round final answers to hundredths.

d) Can we fit one 17-inch straw inside the container without bending it?

1.2 Translations

I. Use smart labels to identify your variables before you write your translation.

1. "The height of the rectangle is 3 inches less than the width of the rectangle."

2. "The product of two numbers is equal to nine more than the larger number."

   $S \cdot L = L + 9$

3. "The sum of two numbers is 14 less than the product of the two numbers."

4. "The length of the rectangular room is 7 feet more than triple the width."

   $L = 7 + 3w$

5. "The quantity four meters less than 5 times the diameter is 101 meters."

6. "The altitude (height) of the triangle is 8 inches less than the length of the rectangle."

   $h = L - 8$

7. "Triple the length of the table is 3 inches more than the height of the doorway."

8. "The radius of the circular patio is no more than 10 feet."

   $r \geq 10$

9. "The radius of the circular patio is 18 inches more than the width of the walkway."

10. "Twice the volume of the pool is at most 2,000 cubic feet."

11. "The longer leg of the right triangle is 2 feet less than double the shorter leg."

12. "The number of student tickets sold is at least 30 more than the number of regular tickets sold."

II. Use the variables as defined and make the necessary unit conversions to write your translation.

1. "The height of the rectangle is 3 inches less than the width." Let h = height (foot), w = width (foot).

2. "The total cost is 48 cents less than the estimated price." Let C = total cost (dollar), e = estimated price (dollar).

3. "six meters less than 5 times the radius" Let r = radius (centimeter).

5r - 600

4. "The leg length of the isosceles triangle is 4 yards more than the base." Let l = leg length (foot), b = base (foot).

5. "The time spent shopping was less than 90 minutes. Let t = time shopping (hour).

6. "Two weeks more than the time left until school break is 48 days." Let t = time left until school break (day).

7. "Seventy centimeters less than the altitude of the triangle is triple the base." Let h = altitude (m), b = base (m).

8. The time the ball has been falling is at most 1.25 minutes." Let t = time the ball has been falling (second).

9. "five centimeters less than 4 times the diameter" Let d = diameter (meter).

4d - 5

10. "Five times the width is 12 feet less than the length." Let W = width (yard), L = length (yard).

11. "The time since the study began is at least 15 months." Let t = time since the study began (year).

12. "The depth of the box is 2.5 feet less than twice the height." Let d = depth (inch), h = height (inch).

d = 2h - 2.5

1.2 Formulas

I. Use the variables as defined to write the specified formula. Draw and label a diagram when appropriate to help you.

1. Perimeter of a rectangle formula. Let P = perimeter, H = height, W = width.

2. Diagonal across a rectangle formula. Let D = diagonal, H = height, W = width.

3. Area of a rectangle formula. Let A = area, H = height, L = length.

4. Perimeter of a closed semicircle formula. Let P = perimeter, r = radius.

5. Area of a closed semicircle formula. Let A = area, d = diameter.

6. Perimeter of a closed quarter-circle formula. Let P = perimeter, d = diameter.

7. Area of a closed quarter-circle formula. Let A = area, r = radius.

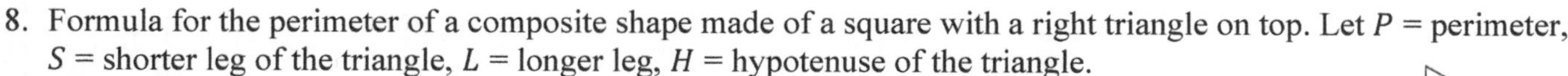

8. Formula for the perimeter of a composite shape made of a square with a right triangle on top. Let P = perimeter, S = shorter leg of the triangle, L = longer leg, H = hypotenuse of the triangle.

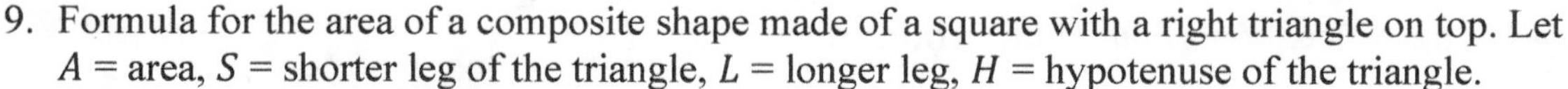

9. Formula for the area of a composite shape made of a square with a right triangle on top. Let A = area, S = shorter leg of the triangle, L = longer leg, H = hypotenuse of the triangle.

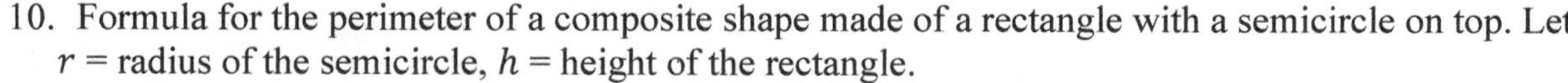

10. Formula for the perimeter of a composite shape made of a rectangle with a semicircle on top. Let r = radius of the semicircle, h = height of the rectangle.

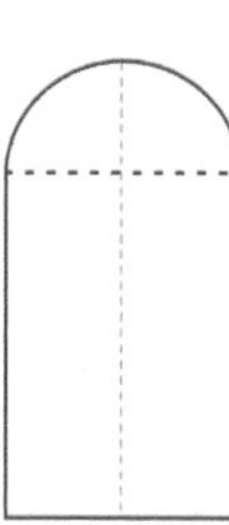

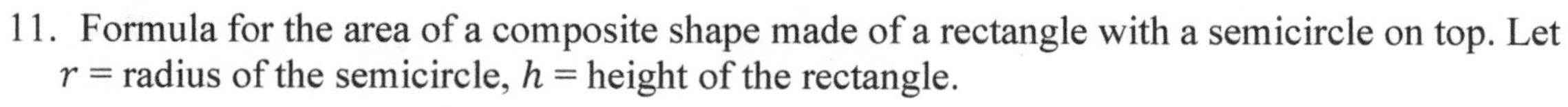

11. Formula for the area of a composite shape made of a rectangle with a semicircle on top. Let r = radius of the semicircle, h = height of the rectangle.

12. Formula for the total length of string needed to make pattern shown at right, including lines inside the rectangle. Let T = total length of string, h = height of the larger, outer rectangle, w = width of the outer rectangle.

13. Formula for the total length of ribbon needed to make pattern shown at right, including lines inside the figure. The figure is an equilateral triangle on top of a rectangle. Let R = total length of ribbon, s = side length of the triangle, h = height of the rectangle.

14. Formula for the total length of fence to enclose a rectangular kennel *and* to divide it into 3 sections. Let F = total length of fence, L = length of one *section* of the kennel, h = width of one *section*.

Dog: Nadya_Art Shutterstock.com

15. Formula for the total area inside a rectangular kennel. Let A = total area inside the kennel, l = length of one *section* of the kennel, w = width of one *section*.

16. Formula for the total trim used around the border of an office, not including the 3.5-foot doorway. Let T = the total trim, L = length of the office, W = width of the office.

Desk: benchmark/Shutterstock.com

17. Formula for the total length of fence to enclose a rectangular plot alongside a river as shown in the figure. No fence is used along the river. Let F = total length of fence, L = length of the plot, W = width of the plot.

II. Use the variables as defined to write the specified formula.

1. A manager buys lunch for the office. She buys burritos, tacos, and waters. The price of one burrito is $6, one taco costs $1.75, and a soda costs $2. Write a formula for the total number of items the manager purchased. Let:

T = total number of items (item)
b = number of burritos (burrito)
t = number of tacos (taco)
w = number of waters (water)

2. A manager buys lunch for the office. She buys burritos, tacos, and waters. The price of one burrito is $6, one taco costs $1.75, and a soda costs $2. Write a formula for the total cost of the manager's purchase. Let:

C = total cost of items (dollar)
b = number of burritos (burrito)
t = number of tacos (taco)
w = number of waters (water)

3. A van is carrying televisions (TVs), laptops, and printers. The weight of one printer is 3 times the weight of one laptop, and one TV weighs 2 times as much as a laptop. Write a formula for the total number of items carried in the van. Let:

T = total number of items in the van (item)
t = number of TVs in the van (TV)
l = number of laptops in the van (laptop)
p = number of printers in the van (printer)

4. A corner shop ordered flowers for Mother's Day. The number of carnations ordered was 100, the number of daisies 400, and the number of roses was 800. Write a formula for the total cost of the flowers. Let:

C = total cost of the flowers (dollar)
c = price of one carnation (dollar per carnation)
d = price of one daisy (dollar per daisy)
r = price of one rose (dollar per rose)

5. A van is carrying 12 televisions (TVs), 32 laptops, and 20 printers. The weight of one printer is 3 times the weight of one laptop, and one TV weighs 2 times as much as a laptop. Write a formula for the total weight carried in the van. Let:

W = total weight of items in the van (pound)
t = weight of one TV (pound)
l = weight of one laptop (pound)
p = weight of one printer (pound)

III. Go back to each formula you wrote in sections I. and II. above and translate the formula into English using your own words.

1.3.A. Problem Solving - Linear

1.3.A. Launch: Building a Deck

Suppose we are building a rectangular deck. We want the area of the deck to be at least 200 square feet but we use exactly 960 inches of trim for the edges. We also want the length of the deck to be five feet less than twice its width.

b) Perform the quantitative analysis. [This part can be completed in section 1.1.]

Constants

Labeled Diagram:

value	unit	detailed description of the quantity

Variables

label	unit	detailed description of the quantity	disc/cont.

b) Translate requirements into symbolic language. Write any other formula(s) that relate the quantities.

c) Try to find correct dimensions of the deck using the guess-n-check method. How can you check your solution? Is this an efficient way to solve the problem?

d). Solve algebraically for the dimensions and for the area of the deck.

1.3.A. Linear Problems

Go back to solve the following linear problems in the workbook:
1.1 Launch: Fencing a Pen, 1.1 Problems #1,2,4
1.2 Launch: Building a Patio, 1.2 Problems #1,2,3

1. *Sergio thinks that he is five years younger than double the age of Chloe. Chloe thinks that she is five years older than half of the age of Sergio. Can they both be correct?*
a) Perform the quantitative analysis. [This part can be completed in a previous section.]

b) Translate the requirements into symbolic language using your labels above. Write any other formula(s) that relate the quantities in this situation. [This part can be completed in the previous section.]

c) Solve the problem algebraically.

d) Explain what happens when we solve the system of equations for this problem. What does that tells us about the solution(s) to the problem?

2. *The shore, a rope, and an 8-meter dock enclose a rectangular swimming area along the lakeshore. The length of the swim area, parallel to the shore, is 6 meters more than the width, and the swim area must be more than 180 square meters. The total length of rope used to enclose the swim area is 34 meters, and the rope is not used along the shore or along the dock.*

a) Perform the quantitative analysis. [This part can be completed in a previous section.]

b) Translate the requirements into symbolic language using your labels above. Write any other formula(s) that relate the quantities in this situation. [This part can be completed in the previous section.]

c) Solve for the dimensions of the swim area algebraically.

d) Verify that your solution satisfies the area requirement for the swimming area. Is it big enough? Justify your answer with calculations.

3. *A shopper spent $62.67 on 12 cans of tuna, a carton of milk, and 7 boxes of cereal. The price of one can of tuna was $2.40 less than the price of the carton of milk and a box of cereal was 81 cents more than the carton of milk. What was the price of the carton of milk? What was the price of one can of tuna? One box of cereal?*

a) Perform the quantitative analysis. [This part can be completed in a previous section.]

units	Descr.	#
$	TOTAL	62.67

	Describ	D/C	smart label
$	Tuna	D	C
$	carton of milk	D	M
$	box of ceral	D	B

units	describ	#
	tuna	12
	milk	1
	cearal	7

b) Translate the requirements into symbolic language using your labels above. Write any other formula(s) that relate the quantities in this situation. [This part can be completed in the previous section.]

$12C + 1M + 7B = 62.67$

c) Solve for the price of each item algebraically.

d) The shopper wants to spend no more than $2 on a can of tuna. Translate this requirement and then verify whether or not the solution satisfies it.

e) The shopper expects to spend at least $5 on a box of cereal. Translate this requirement and then verify whether or not the solution satisfies it.

1.3.A. Solving Linear Equations and Systems

I. Solve each linear equation. Show all work.

1. $5 + 3(5 + 2x) + x = 14 + 2(x + 2) + 7$

5. $5(x - 2) + 3x = 2(7 - x - 5x) + 6$

2. $-13t + \frac{1}{2} + 3t = 4 - 20t$

6. $6n - (5n - 8) = 1 - (12 - 3n)$

3. $p - 20 + 4p + 3p = -(2 - 7p + 11)$

7. $2(9 + y) = 4(2y + 1) - (7 - y)$

4. $7(x - 2) = -3(2 + x)$

8. $4 - 2(t - 5) = 3t - 4(t + 2)$

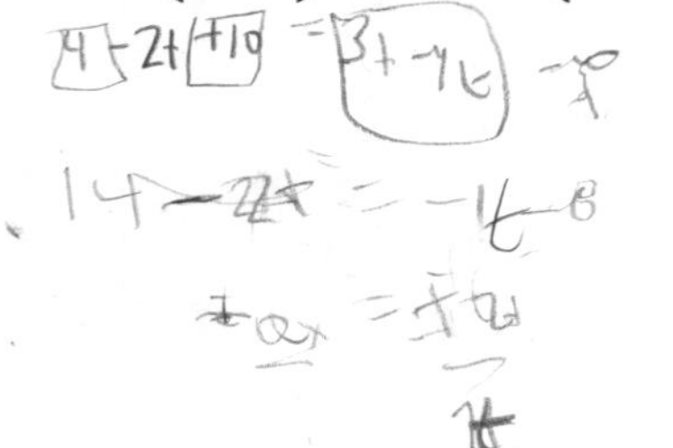

II. Solve each linear system by substitution. Show all work.

1. $\begin{cases} x = 2y + 2 \\ 53y + 9x = 1012 \end{cases}$

4. $\begin{cases} b = a - 85 \\ c = 9a + 8 \\ 7a - b + 6c = 6133 \end{cases}$

2. $\begin{cases} y = 3t - 5 \\ 5t - 2y = 112 \end{cases}$

5. $\begin{cases} x = 23y - 15 \\ z = y + 24 \\ 2x - y + 14z = 2843 \end{cases}$

3. $\begin{cases} 4a - 3 = b \\ -a - 6b = 63 \end{cases}$

6. $\begin{cases} L = 5D - 6 \\ W = D + 1 \\ 7L + 4W + 3D = 676 \end{cases}$

7. $\begin{cases} p = 2r - 1 \\ q = 2r + 1 \\ 3p + 2q + r = 4.5 \end{cases}$

8. $\begin{cases} w = c + 6 \\ c = w - 5 \end{cases}$

9. $\begin{cases} \frac{1}{2}y - 3x = 100 \\ y = 14x \end{cases}$

10. $\begin{cases} x = 5z - 4 \\ y = z + 7 \\ x - 5y = z \end{cases}$

1.3.B. Problem Solving – NON-Linear

1.3.B. NON-Linear Problems

Go back to solve the following NON-linear problems in the workbook:
1.1 Problem #3, 1.2 Problem #4

1. *A television screen measures 55.07 inches on the diagonal, and its height is* $\frac{9}{16}$ *of its width. What are the perimeter and area of the screen?*
a) Perform the quantitative analysis. Draw and label a diagram. [This part can be completed in a previous section.]

b) Translate the requirements into symbolic language using your labels above. Write any other formula(s) that relate the quantities in this situation. [This part can be completed in the previous section.]

c) Solve the problem algebraically. Round final answers to the nearest hundredth.

2. *A right triangular (artificial) pond is part of a city landscape. The shorter leg is ¼ times as long as the longer leg. The surface area of the pond is at least 2600 square feet but less than 4000 square feet. Find the perimeter of the pond.*

a) Perform the quantitative analysis. [This part can be completed in a previous section.]. Ducks: Golden Vector/Shutterstock.com

b) Translate the requirements into symbolic language using your labels above. Write any other formula(s) that relate the quantities in this situation. [This part can be completed in the previous section.]

c) *Suppose the area of the pond is exactly 3,000 square feet.* Find its side-lengths algebraically. Round final answers to the nearest hundredth.

d) Find the perimeter of the pond. Show all calculations.

3. *Kenesha has a box-shaped lap pool with a width that is twice its depth and length that is twelve times its depth. The volume of water in the pool is no more than 2,000 cubic feet.*

a) Perform the quantitative analysis. [This part can be completed in a previous section.]

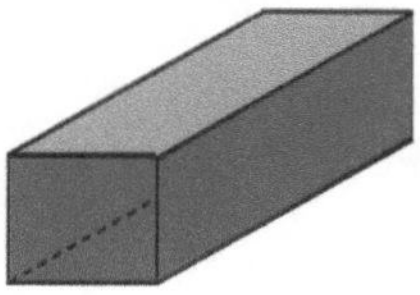

b) Translate the requirements into symbolic language using your labels above. Write any other formula(s) that relate the quantities in this situation. [This part can be completed in the previous section.]

c) Suppose the volume of the pool is exactly 1,700 cubic feet. Find its dimensions algebraically. Round final answers to the nearest hundredth.

4. *A tent has the shape of a right triangular prism. The altitude of the triangular base is* $\frac{3}{4}$ *of the base of that triangle, and the length of the tent is 2 times the base of the triangular base. If the volume of the tent is 384 cubic feet, what are its dimensions?*

a) Perform the quantitative analysis. [This part can be completed in a previous section.]

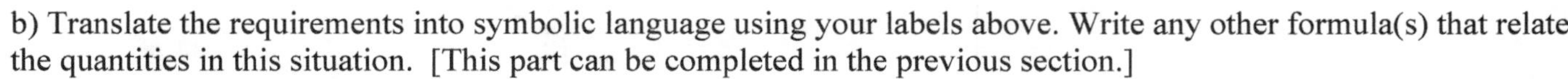

b) Translate the requirements into symbolic language using your labels above. Write any other formula(s) that relate the quantities in this situation. [This part can be completed in the previous section.]

c) Find the base and the height of the tent algebraically. Round final answers to the nearest hundredth.

1.3.B. Solving NON-Linear Equations and Systems

I. Solve each NON-linear equation. Show all work.

1. $3h^2 = 75$

2. $8v^2 + 4v^2 = 98$

3. $9 + t^3 = 2000$

4. $\frac{4}{5}d^2 = 800$

5. $1300 = 8b^3 + 100$

6. $540 = 15W^2 - 7W^2$

7. $(5H)^2H = 675$

8. $(5s)^2 + s^2 = 775$

9. $(6r)9r^2 = 1188$

10. $-7t^2 + 9t^2 + 12 = 54$

11. $900 = (8w)(7.5w)(w)$

12. $5045 = (\frac{2}{3}D)(12D)$

13. $2486 = (2L)^2 + (3L)^2$

14. $\left(\frac{1}{4}L\right)\left(\frac{1}{2}L\right)L = 216{,}000$

15. $4s^2 + 8s^2 = 8{,}427$

16. $(6t)^2 - (2t)(5t) + 95t^2 = 484$

II. Solve each NON-linear system by substitution. Show all work.

1. $\begin{cases} l = 5w \\ lw = 125 \end{cases}$

2. $\begin{cases} L = 3D \\ W = \frac{1}{2}D \\ LWD = 2{,}592 \end{cases}$

3. $\begin{cases} a = 7c \\ b = 2c \\ a^2 + b^2 = 2{,}239.25 \end{cases}$

4. $\begin{cases} x = \frac{3}{4}y \\ \frac{2}{9}x^2y = 1 \end{cases}$

5. $\begin{cases} 95{,}256 = 8LW \\ L = 12W \end{cases}$

$95{,}256 = 8(12w)w$

$95{,}256 = 96w \cdot w$

$\frac{95{,}256}{96} = \frac{96w^2}{96}$

$\pm\sqrt{992.25} = \sqrt{w^2}$

$\pm 31.5 = w$

$L = 12(-31.5) = 378$

-378

6. $\begin{cases} W^2 + H^2 = 3438.5 \\ H = 5W \end{cases}$

1.3.A-B. Problem Solving - Mixed

1.3.A-B. Critical Thinking

1. *Mateo has 14 meters of fence for a rectangular pen alongside of his house. He only needs to fence three sides such that the length is 1 meter less than triple the width. The pen is for his dog that needs more than 20 square meters to be happy. What are the dimensions of the pen?*

a) Perform the quantitative analysis. Draw and label a diagram. [This part can be completed in a previous section.]

b) Translate the requirements into symbolic language using your labels above. Write any other formula(s) that relate the quantities in this situation. [This part can be completed in the previous section.]

c) Find the dimensions of the pen algebraically. Round final answers to the nearest hundredth.

d) Verify whether or not your solution satisfies the area requirement. Show the calculations to justify your answer.

e) Show another way to set up the problem. Does it lead to the same answer?

2. *Sunny Days apartment building has a cylindrical, above ground pool with a diameter that is six times its height. If the volume of the pool is 2,576.5 cubic feet, what is the radius of the pool?*

a) Perform the quantitative analysis. [This part can be completed in a previous section.]

b) Translate the requirements into symbolic language using your labels above. Write any other formula(s) that relate the quantities in this situation. [This part can be completed in the previous section.]

c) Find the height (depth) and the radius of the pool algebraically.

3. *Pam has a box-shaped lap pool two times wider than it is deep and six times longer than it is wide. The water charge to fill the pool is \$6 per 100 cubic feet. If Pam spends \$92.16 to fill the pool, how deep is it?*

a) Perform the quantitative analysis. [This part can be completed in a previous section.]

pool

b) Translate the requirements into symbolic language using your labels above. Write any other formula(s) that relate the quantities in this situation. [This part can be completed in the previous section.]

c) Find the depth of the pool algebraically.

d) *Pam has a box-shaped lap pool two times wider than it is deep and six times longer than it is wide, as above. The water charge to fill the pool is \$6 per 100 cubic feet. If Pam wants to spend at most \$100 to fill it, is a 5-foot deep pool affordable?* Justify your answer with calculations.

1.3.A-B. More Mixed Problems

1. *Zofia has a box-shaped pool. Its width is triple its depth and its length is double its width. The floor of the pool measures exactly 761.76 square feet. Find the volume of the pool.*

2. *A rectangular field has a length that is triple its width and a diagonal of 98 meters. Find its area.*

3. *The diagram at right shows a Norman window which has the outline of a semicircle on top of a rectangle. The height of the rectangle is three times the width of the rectangle. If the exact area of the glass that covers the entire window is 102.62 square feet, what is the width of the rectangular part of the window? What is the radius of the semicircle? If the builders can use no more than 45 feet of trim for the perimeter, do they have enough?*

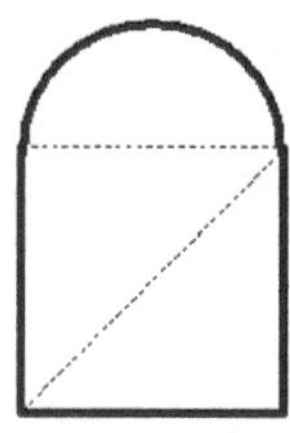

4. *Each side of a triangular garden has a different length. The longest side is 4 feet longer than the mid-length side, and the shortest side is 27 inches shorter than the mid-length side. Find the length of each side of the garden if its perimeter is 100 feet.*

5. *A manager spends $102.68 on lunch for the office. She buys a total of 47 items - 12 burritos, 20 tacos, and 15 sodas. A burrito costs $1.20 more than a taco, and one soda costs 35 cents less than a taco. How much does each item cost?*

6. *To qualify for a new job, a student took three self-paced, online training courses at different times. He spent one week less on the first course than on the second course, and he spent 2 weeks more on the third course than on the second. Altogether he spent 75 days taking the three courses. How much time did he spend on each course?*

7. *The total tickets sales for one day of the Spring Fair was $3,570. That day the number of senior tickets sold was 265 less than the number of adult tickets sold, and the number of child tickets sold was 10 more than twice the number of adult tickets. A child's ticket costs $1.25, an adult ticket costs $5, and a senior ticket is $2.50. How many of each kind of ticket was sold?*

8. *A homeowner is carpeting a room whose shape is a right triangle next to a square as shown in the figure. The side length of the square is the same as the longer leg of the right triangle, and the shorter leg is $\frac{3}{4}$ times the longer leg. If the total area of the floor is 665.5 square feet, what is the longer leg of the triangle (side length of the square)? How long is the shorter leg?*

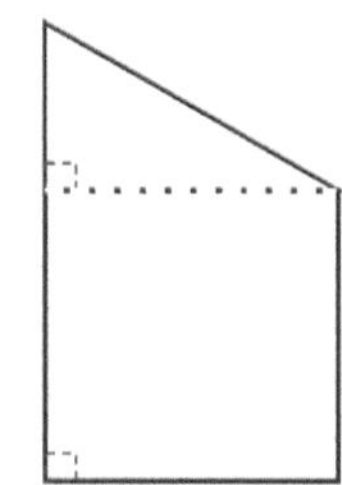

9. *A rectangular entryway has a temporary support beam across its diagonal. The width of the entryway is $\frac{3}{4}$ of its height. If the support beam across the diagonal is 17.5 feet long, what are the dimensions of the entryway?*

10. *A student spent a total of 3.25 hours studying, then eating lunch, then walking to a friend's house. The time she spent studying was 2 minutes less than four times the time she spent eating lunch. She spent 5 minutes more walking to her friend's house than she did eating lunch. How much time did she spend doing each activity?*

11. *A teacher is using ribbon to create an outline on the bulletin board as shown in the figure at right. Each section has the shape of an equilateral triangle. The total area inside the large triangle is 4,330 square centimeters. The altitude (height) of a small triangle is 0.866 times its side length. What is the side length of the small triangles in the pattern? What is the altitude of the small triangles?*

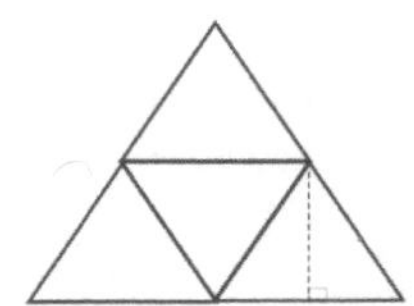

12. *A ladder is leaning against a wall such that its top is at the top of the wall. Assume the wall is perpendicular to the ground. The distance from the base of the ladder to the wall is 19.5 feet, and the ladder is 1.25 times the height of the wall. What is the height of the wall? How long is the ladder?*

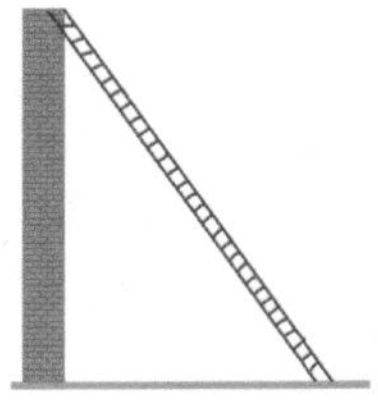

13. *A storage container has the shape of a cylinder. The height of the container is 4 times its radius, and the volume is 1,144.53 cubic inches. What is the radius of the container? What is its height?*

14. *A shipping carton has the shape of a right triangular prism whose base is a right triangle. The depth of the carton is 5 times the shorter leg of the base, and the longer leg of the base is 2 times the shorter leg. If the volume of the carton is 3,645 cubic centimeters, what are its dimensions?*

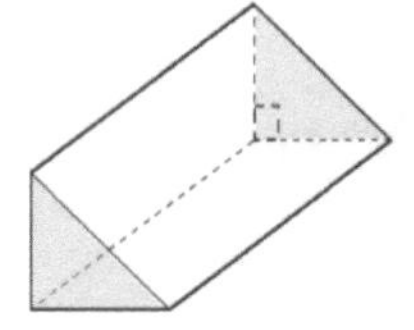

15. *An above ground pool has the shape of a cylinder. The diameter of the pool is 8 times its height, and the volume is 3,215.36 cubic feet. What is the height of the pool? What is its radius?*

16. *A farmer encloses a rectangular plot of land along a river with its length along the river as shown in the figure. The width of the plot is 5 feet more than half of the length, and no fence is used along the river. If the total fence used to enclose the plot is 882 feet, what is the length of the plot? What is the width? The area?*

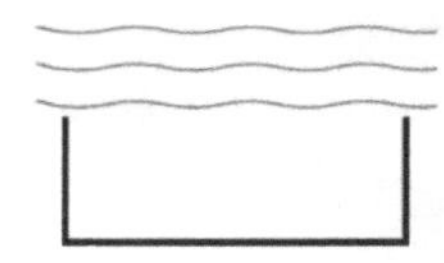

17. *A window has the shape of a closed quarter-circle and measures 149.94 centimeters around its border. What is the radius of the quarter-circle? What is its area?*

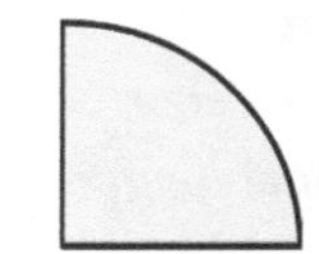

18. *A cabinet maker is going to build a bookcase like the one shown in the figure. The height of the bookcase is 10 inches less than the length of the bookcase. The total length of board needed to cut the shelves and the sides, including the top and the bottom is 368 inches. What is the length of the bookcase? What is its height?*

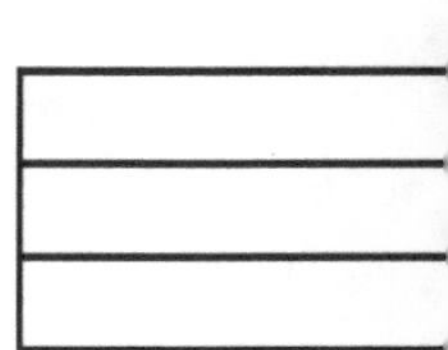

19. *Matilda covers the interior faces of a kitchen drawer with shelf paper. The height of the drawer is 3/4 its width and the depth front to back is 7/4 its width. If the exact amount of shelf paper needed is 846 square inches, what is the depth of the drawer?*

20. A rectangle and an isosceles triangle have the same perimeter. The length of the rectangle is four times the width. The legs of the triangle are each 21 feet more than the base of the triangle. The base of the triangle is the same as the width of the rectangle. What are all of the side lengths for each figure?

21. Alice, Brian, Colin, and Dave each buy some lottery tickets. Alice buys half as many tickets as Brian. Colin buys three times as many tickets as Brian, and Dave buys four more than four times as many tickets as Brian. If the tickets cost $2 each and together they spent exactly $416, then how many tickets did they each buy?

22. In a cash register, there are one-dollar bills, five dollar bills, ten-dollar bills and twenty-dollar bills. The total amount in the register is $474. There are three times as many ten-dollar bills as twenty-dollar bills. The number of fives is two less than the number of singles. Altogether, there are 58 bills in the register. How many of each bill is there?

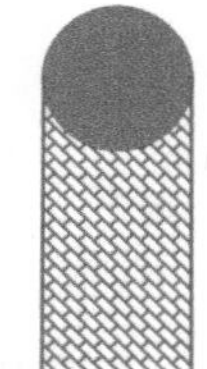

23. Ms. Smith is building a circular pool right next to a rectangular patio as shown in the figure. The width of the rectangular patio is exactly the same as the diameter of the pool, and the length of the patio is three times its width. It took 44 feet of tile to go around the edge of the pool. How many square feet of tile will it take to cover the patio?

24. [Harvard 1869] A man bought a watch, a chain, and a medallion with $216. The watch and the medallion together cost three times the chain. The chain and the medallion together cost half the watch. What was the price of each?

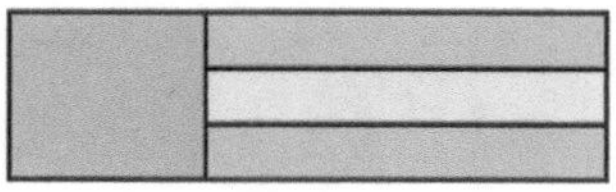

25. One of the club teams on campus is making a flag for their team as shown in the figure below (not drawn to scale.) The blue section is a square. The striped sections are all exactly the same size, and the length of each striped section is six times as long as the width of each striped section. The club uses black ribbon to trim around the outside edge and to trim all of the lines between sections. If they use 351 inches of black ribbon, what is the area for the entire flag?

26. Nat used 366 feet of fencing to enclose a rectangular garden and to put a divider between the two halves of the garden - the vegetable side and the herb side. The width of the garden is 18 feet less than its total length (diagram not drawn to scale). Figure out the dimensions of the entire garden and then find the area of each half of the garden. Plants: Andrii Bezvershenko/Shutter-stock.com

Self-Assessment Test 1: Problem Solving

1. *Cole used 58 feet of fencing to create a pen and its dividers. She used the fence around the perimeter of the pen and for the two dividers to make three equal sections. The total length of the pen is 12 inches more than 2 times its width. She needs the total area of the pen to be at least 100 square feet.*

a) Perform the quantitative analysis. Identify and describe the variables and constants including units

units	D/C	variable
m	continous	l
ft	Continous	w

#	units	description
58	ft	total fencing
100	ft^2	Total AREA

animals: Biscotto Design/Shutterstock.com

b) Translate the requirements into equations and inequalities. Write any other related formulas.

$$\begin{cases} l = 2w + 1 \\ 58 = 4w + 2l \\ A \geq 100 \end{cases}$$

c) Solve for the dimensions and for the area of the entire pen.

$A \geq 100 = L \times W$

$58 = 4w + 2w + 1 + 2w + 1$

$8w$

d) Does your solution satisfy all the requirements? Explain and show calculations to justify your answer.

2. *Ari, Be, and Chun have all earned some reward points from Shopper's World. Ari has earned 55 points less than 6 times Chun's points; Be has earned 15 points more than triple the number of Chun's points. Altogether, they have earned a total of 610 points.*

a) Perform the quantitative analysis.

b) Translate the requirements into equations. Write any other related formulas.

c) Solve for the number of points each of them has earned.

3. *Chris is planning a box-shaped pool with a width that is twice its depth and a length 4 times its depth. The volume of the pool must be exactly 125 cubic meters.*

15pts

a) Perform the quantitative analysis.

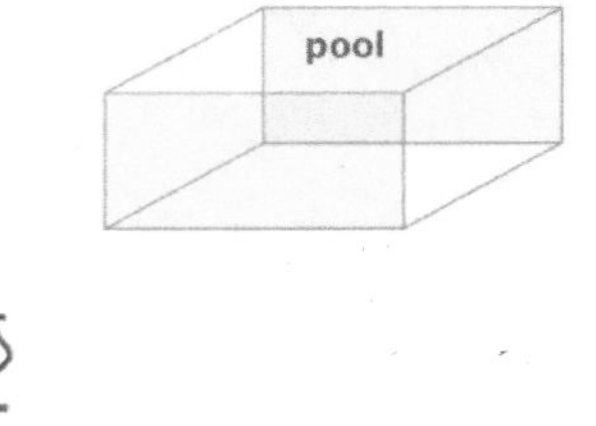

constant	units	Description
125	m3	volume of pool

variable	units	Descriptions	discrete or continous
w	m	width of pool	continous
l	m	lenght of pool	continous

9pts

b) Translate the requirements into equations and inequalities. Write any other related formulas.

$$\begin{cases} w = 2d \\ l = 4d \\ 125^{m3} = w \cdot l \cdot d \end{cases}$$

4pts

c) Solve for the depth of the pool.

$$125^{m3} = (2d)\cdot(4d)\cdot d$$

$$\frac{125^{m3}}{8} = \frac{8d^3}{8}$$

$$\sqrt[3]{15.625} = \sqrt[3]{d^3}$$

2pts $2.5m = d$

30 pts

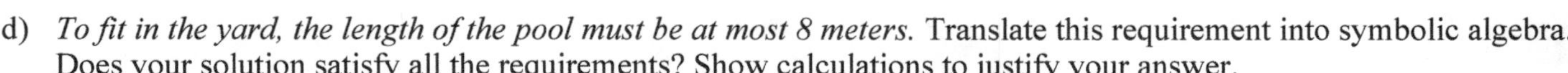

d) *To fit in the yard, the length of the pool must be at most 8 meters.* Translate this requirement into symbolic algebra. Does your solution satisfy all the requirements? Show calculations to justify your answer.

Answer Key Test 1

1. a) Constants: 100 sq. feet – minimum area; 58 feet – fencing; Variables: L – the total length of pen – foot; W – the width of pen – foot; A – the area of pen – sq. foot;
   b) Translations: $L = 2W + 1$; $58 = 2L + 4W$; $A \geq 100$; Related Formula: $A = LW$
   c) $W = 7$ feet; $L = 15$ feet; $A = 105$ sq. feet;
   d) Yes since $A = 105$ and $105 > 100$;

2. a). Constant: 610 points – total number of pts.; Variables: A – Ari's number of pts. – points; B – Be's number of pts. – points; C – Chun's number of pts. – points
   b) Translations: $A = 6C - 55$; $B = 3C + 15$; Total points formula: $A + B + C = 610$
   c) $A = 335$ pts; $B = 210$ pts; $C = 65$ pts.

3. a) Constant: 125 cu. meters – the volume of pool; Variables: d – the depth of pool – m; W – the width of pool – m; L – the length of pool – m;
   b) Translations: $W = 2d$; $L = 4d$; Volume Formula: $125 = LWd$;
   c) $d = 2.5$ m;
   d) No since $L = 10$ and $10 > 8$;

1.4.A. Introduction to Modeling with Functions

1.4.A. Launch: Buying Protein Bars

A hike leader is going to buy protein bars that cost $5 each. Her team will not need more than 20 bars. How much money will she spend on protein bars?

a) Perform a quantitative analysis with two variables. Notice that the value of one variable, which we call the *dependent variable*, depends on the value of the other variable, called the *dependent variable*. Identify which variable is independent (IV), and which is dependent (DV).

b) The hike leader is free to choose the value of the independent variable. List the set of all possible choices. This set is called the **domain**.

c) List the set of all possible values for the dependent variable. This set is called the **range**.

IV	DV

d) Match the values of the independent variable with those of the dependent variable in a two-column table (below). List a sample of values for the independent variable in the left column and the corresponding values of the dependent variable in the right column. This matching is called a **relation**.

e) Discuss how we can answer the question and how this problem is different from those in previous sections.

WAIT. Skip to problem (1), circular patio, and problems for quantitative analysis. Then return to sketch graphs.

f) Sketch a graph of the protein bar model.

1.4.A. Quantitative Analysis for Modeling

I. *A home owner is planning to pave a circular patio for her square back yard which measures 50 by 50 feet. What could be the area of the patio?*

a) Perform a quantitative analysis with two variables. Identify which variable is independent (IV), and which is dependent (DV). Use function notation.

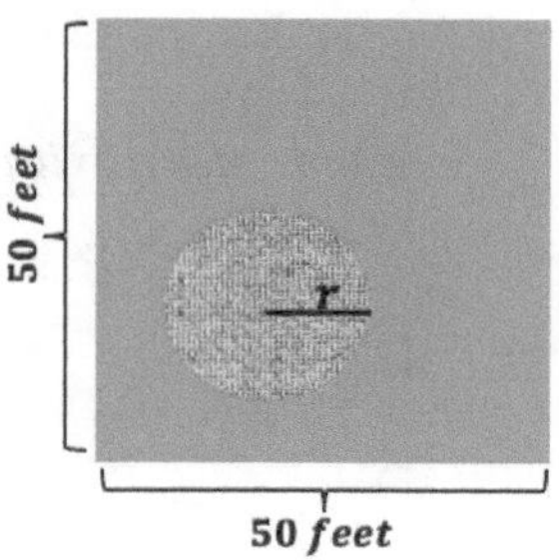

b) Write a related formula that connects the two variables.

IV	DV

c) Start a table to list some ordered pairs of the form (input, output). Include the smallest and largest input values. Round numbers to the nearest tenth.

d) Determine and describe the set of all possible inputs (domain) and the set of all possible outputs (range). Can we list all values?

e) Discuss how we can answer the question and how this problem is different from those in previous sections.

WAIT. Skip to problems for quantitative analysis. Then return to sketch graphs.

f) Sketch a graph of the circular patio model.

II. There is a functional relationship between two variables in each situation. For each situation:
a) Identify and label the independent and dependent variables. Use function notation.
b) Start a table including the end values of the variables (initial, final, max, min).
c) Are the domain and range discrete or continuous? Explain.
d) Write the domain and range including units. Use notation consistent with part (c).

1. *A tank starts with 5 ounces of water and we start to pour water into it. After 1 hour there are 125 ounces in the tank.*

IV	DV

IV:

DV:

Enter the initial and final ordered pairs of the story into the table.

Choose *any* value between 5 and 125 ounces. Will the tank contain exactly that amount of water at some moment in time? If your answer is no, give an example.

Are the domain and range continuous or discrete? Explain why.

Domain:

Range:

2. *I begin with 5 marbles in a bag. After each minute I add two marbles to the bag for one full hour.*

IV:

DV:

Choose *any* value between 5 and 125 marbles. Will the bag contain exactly that amount of amount at some moment in time? If your answer is no, give an example.

Are the domain and range continuous or discrete? Explain why.

Domain:

Range:

3. *A campus club has 400 shirts to sell in their fundraiser. The club earns 10 dollars in profit for every t-shirt they sell. Before they sell any shirts the profit is $– 3600.*

IV: T-Shirts = T

DV: profit in $'s = D

function notation f(x) = p(s)

T	D
1	10
2	20

Are the variables continuous or discrete? Explain.
The variables are discrete because you can count them.

Domain: {0, 1, 2, ..., 399, 400} # of shirts

Range: {-3600, -3590 ... 394400} profit in $'s

4. *The oven started at 70 degrees Fahrenheit. Once turned on it took 10 minutes to heat to of 420°F.*

IV:

DV:

Are the variables continuous or discrete? Explain.

Domain:

Range:

5. *A bakery starts a day with 90 cupcakes and on average, they sell 6 cupcakes every hour for 10 hours.* Describe the variables so that the initial value is 0 cupcakes.

IV:

DV:

Are the variables continuous or discrete? Explain.

Domain:

Range:

6. *A bakery starts a day with 90 cupcakes and on average, they sell 6 cupcakes every hour for 10 hours.* Describe the variables so that the initial value is the 90 cupcakes.

IV:

DV:

Are the variables continuous or discrete? Explain.

Domain:

Range:

III. More Situations

There is a functional relationship between two variables in each situation. For each situation:
a) Identify and label the independent and dependent variables. Use function notation.
b) Start a table including the end values of the variables (initial, final, max, min).
c) Are the domain and range discrete or continuous? Explain.
d) Write the domain and range including units. Use notation consistent with part (c).

7. The temperature was 3 °F below zero at 8am. Then it warmed to 57 °F by 2pm.

8. By 1pm a plane had already flown 80 miles, then it flew another 7 hours for a total of 3,930 miles flown.

9. A vendor had 200 plants to sell. Before she sells any plants her profit is – $1,000, and then she earns $12 in profit for each plant. Her total profit from selling all 200 plants is $1,400.

10. A pool took 15 hours to drain. It started with 18,000 gallons of water in it.

11. A pool is full with 7,500 gallons of water in it and is drained. After half an hour there are 2500 gallons left in the pool. It is empty after 45 minutes.

12. An anchor is lifted from the ocean floor, at 200 feet below sea-level, up to the deck of the ship. After half of a minute the anchor is still 140 feet below sea-level. It takes 110 seconds to lift the anchor to the ship's deck which is 20 feet above sea-level. The surface of the ocean is at a sea-level of 0 feet.

13. The population of a town was 18,000 in the year 2010 and it has been decreasing by 1.3% each year. This trend is expected to continue until 2035 when this model predicts the population will be about 12,978.

14. A person is on a deck and throws a ball from 30 feet above the ground. The ball goes up to a maximum height of 36.25 feet after 5/8 of a second, and then falls to the ground after about 2.13 seconds.

IV. Function Notation

Go back over situations (1) – (14) above and write at least two ordered pairs using function notation.

1.4.A. Sketching Graphs

Sketching a Graph

- Draw the horizontal axis and label it with the input variable, inlcuding unit.
- Draw the vertical axis and label it with the output variable, including unit.
- Plot the endpoints matching the end values of the domain and range. Plot a few more data points.
- Conncect the points by a discrete dotted or a continuous solid line as appropriate.
- Mark the axes with the coordinates of each point you plot; pay attention to scales.

I. Return to the 1.4 Launch: Buying Protein Bars and to problem (I) modeling a circular patio and sketch the graphs of those models using the steps above.

II. In the space below, sketch graphs for the models (1) – (6) in section II of Quantitative Analysis for Modeling. Note that you may not know the true pattern/shape of the graph, but you can make a general sketch.

1. filling a tank

2. marbles in a bag

3. selling shirts

4. heating an oven

5. selling cupcakes I

6. selling cupcakes II

1.4.B. Introduction to Modeling with Functions

1.4.B. Domain and Range from Graphs

1. Below are graphs of the *Buying Protein Bars* model. Use the graphs to explain in your own words how to find the domain and range of a *discrete* function from its graph. Write the domain and range for the function.

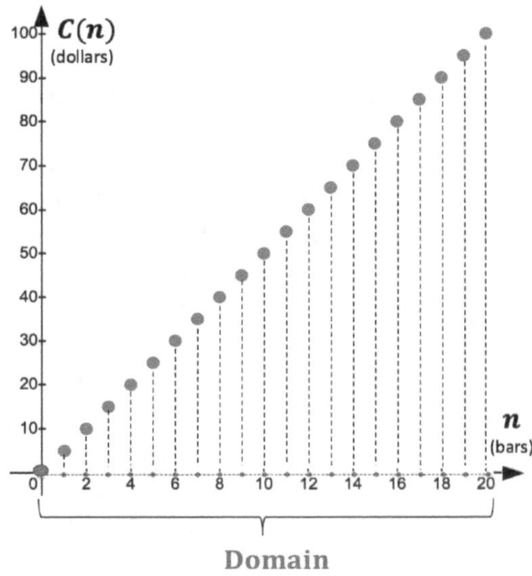

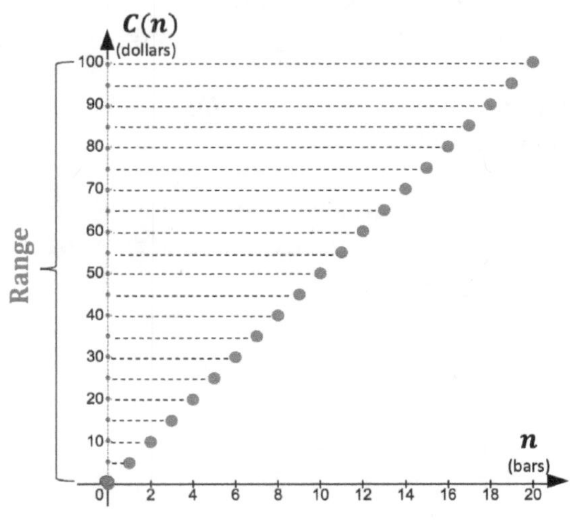

2. Below are graphs of a *Draining a Tank* model. Use the graphs to explain in your own words how to find the domain and range of a *continuous* function from its graph. Write the domain and range for the function.

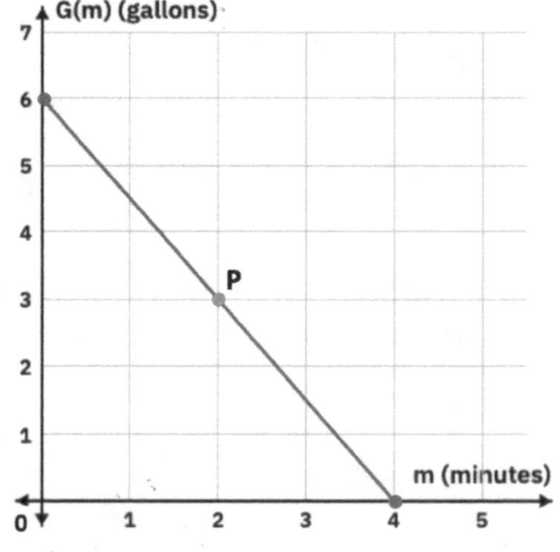

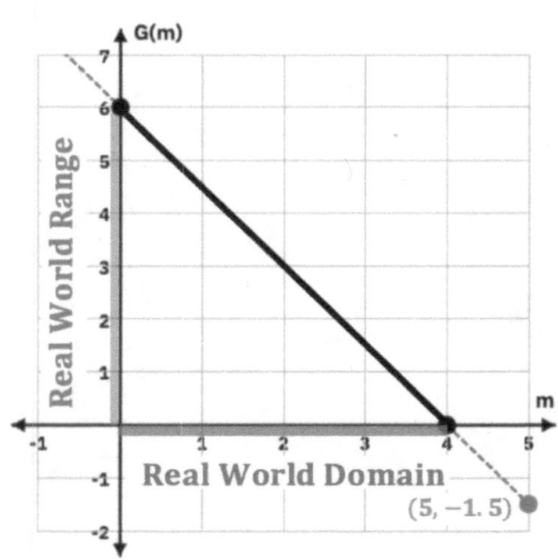

1.4.B. Analyzing Graphs

- Describe the trend of the function: increasing, decreasing, or neither.
- Describe the IV and DV including units so that they are consistent with the trend.
- Start a table and include end values of the variables.
- Write the domain and range including units; use appropriate notation for discrete or continuous sets.
- Find and interpret the vertical and horizontal intercepts

1. Trend:

IV:

DV:

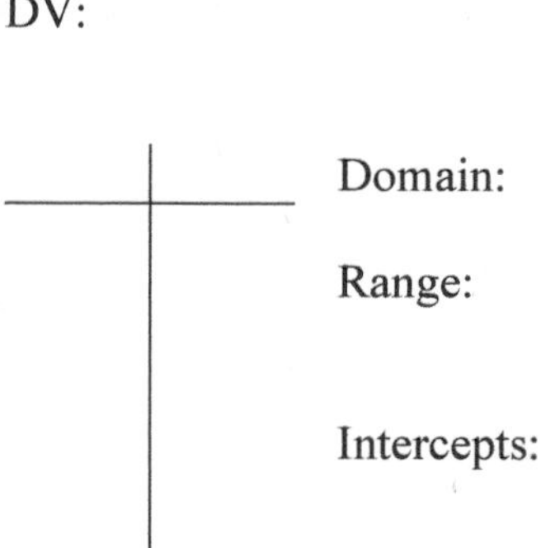

Domain:

Range:

Intercepts:

1.

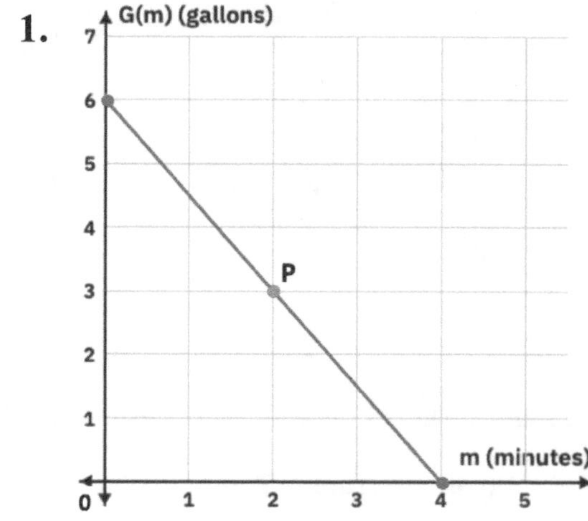

Find answers to the following questions from the graph and write them using function notation.

a) Approximately how many gallons are left in the tank after 1 minute?

b) After about how much time are there 1.5 gallons left?

c) How long does it take to empty the tank?

d) How much liquid was in the tank to begin with?

2. Trend:

IV:

DV:

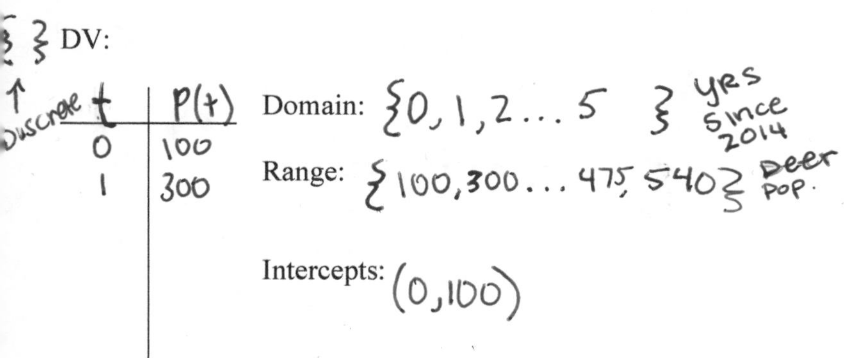

Domain: {0, 1, 2 ... 5} yes since 2014

Range: {100, 300 ... 475, 540} Deer pop.

Intercepts: (0,100)

2.

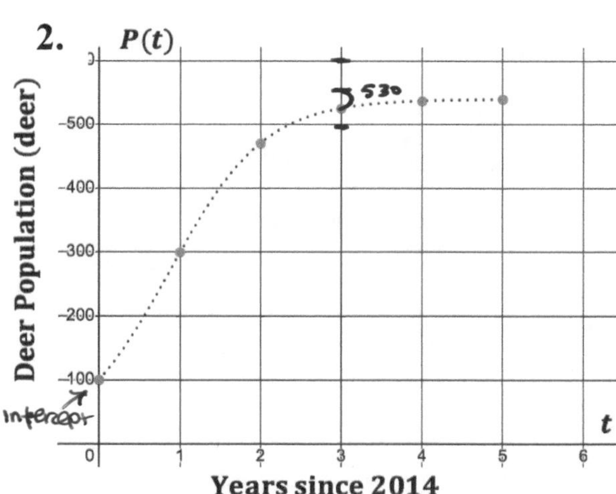

Find answers to the following questions from the graph and write them using function notation.

a) Find and interpret the initial value of the function.

b) Estimate the deer population in 2017.

c) In what year was the deer population approximately 300?

d) Estimate the deer population in 2022.

3. Trend:

IV:

DV:

Domain:

Range:

Intercepts:

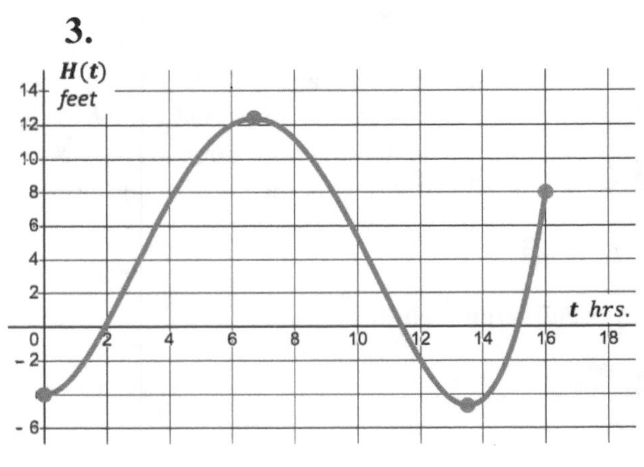

Find answers to the following questions from the graph and write them using function notation.

a) Find and interpret the initial value of the function.

b) At what time(s) is the tide's height approximately –2 feet?

c) How high will the tide be at 4am?

d) Approximately what is the minimum height of the tide?

4. Trend:

IV:

DV:

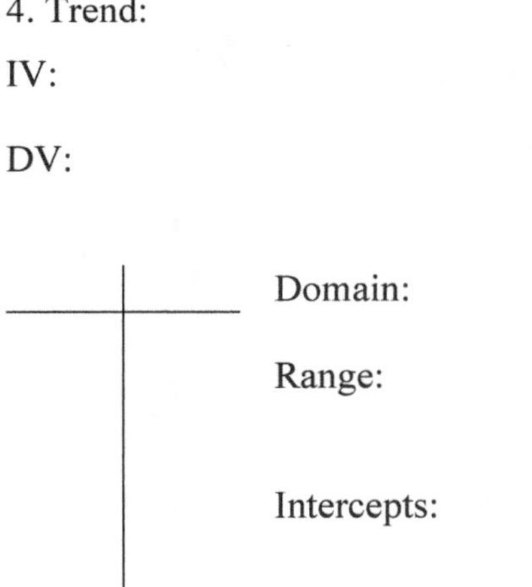

Domain:

Range:

Intercepts:

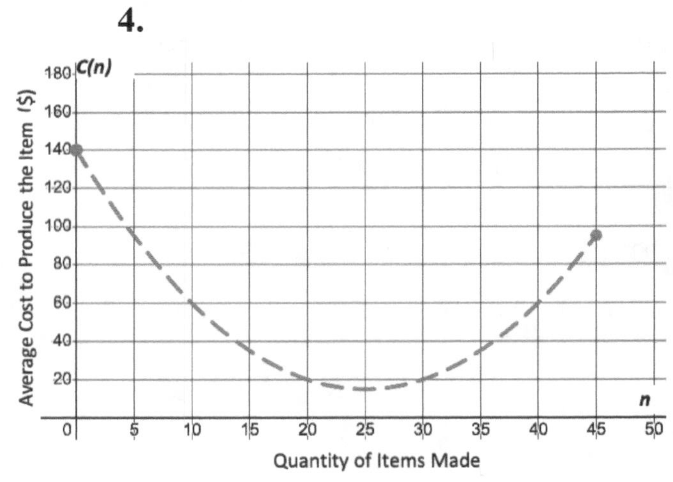

Find answers to the following questions from the graph and write them using function notation.

a) Find and interpret the initial value of the function.

b) If 30 items are made, what will be the average cost to make the item?

c) If the average cost is $60, how many items were made?

d) Approximately what is the minimum average cost to produce the item?

1.4.B. What is a Function?

Define: **A relation:**

A function:

I. Analyzing Relations Using Tables

1. Members of a club are matched with their birth month, student ID, and classes taken. Data is presented below in the form of three sets of ordered pairs. Each set is a relation.

$M = \{(\text{Om, Apr}), (\text{Matt, May}), (\text{Lubna, Jun}), (\text{Asya, Apr})\}$

$N = \{(\text{Om}, 8310), (\text{Matt}, 5108), (\text{Lubna}, 4195), (\text{Asya}, 0981)\}$

$S = \{(\text{Om, MATH}), (\text{Matt, CHEM}), (\text{Lubna, HIST}), (\text{Asya, ENG}), (\text{Asya, ART})\}$

Enter the ordered pairs for each relation in the appropriate table. Explain which of the three relations are functions using the definition. Be specific.

A. Relation ***M***

Input Student x	Output Birth Month M

B. Relation ***N***

Input Student x	Output ID Number N

C. Relation ***S***

Input Student x	Output Subject S

2. Use the definition of a function to explain whether or not each of the following tables represents a function.

a)

x	square of x
−2	4
−1	1
0	0
1	1
2	4

b)

x	square root of x
0	0
1	1
1	−1
4	2
4	−2

c)

x	cube root of x
−8	−2
−1	−1
0	0
1	1
8	2

II. Analyzing Relations Using Graphs

1. Use the definition of a function to explain why each function does or does not represent a function. Be specific. You may create a table of a sample of the ordered pairs to support your explanation.

1.

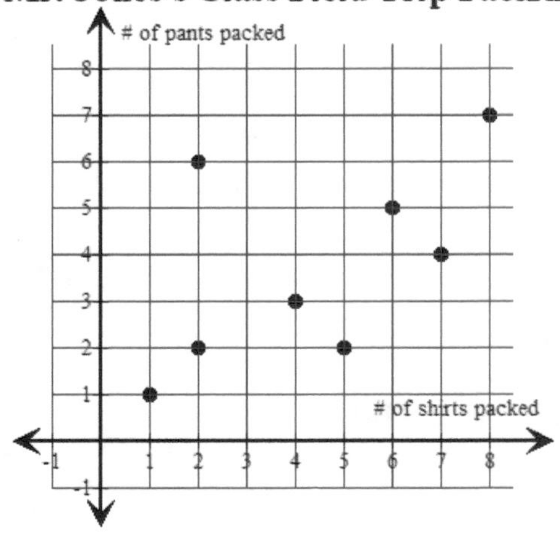

2.

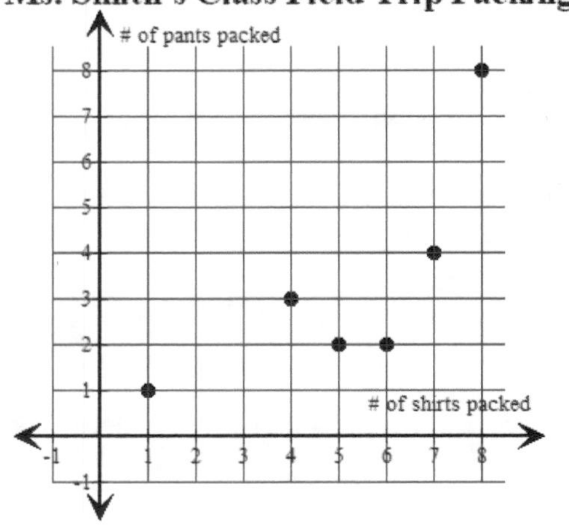

3.

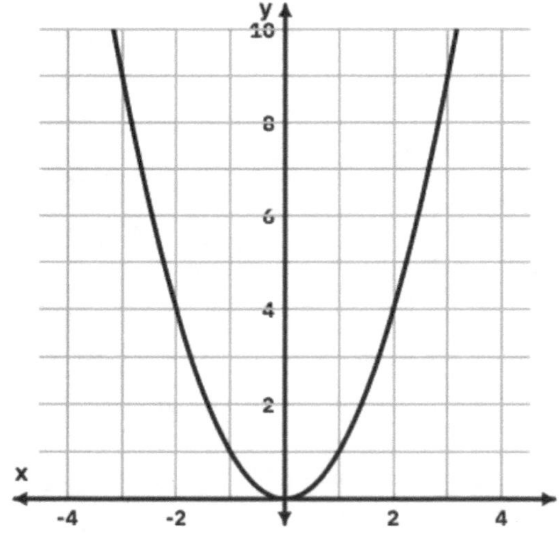

4.

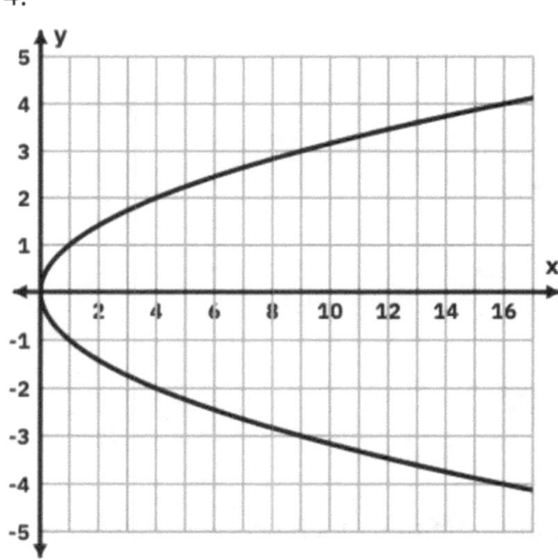

1.4.B. Function Equations

A **function equation** is an equation in two variables, one independent, say x, and one dependent, say $f(x)$, which expresses $f(x)$ as a formula in terms of x.

I. Recall the *Buying Protein Bars* Launch: *A hike leader is going to buy protein bars that cost $5 each. Her team will not need more than 20 bars. How much money will she spend on protein bars?*

a) Write a function equation for the cost function of the protein bars.

b) Use substitution to verify whether or not each ordered pair is a solution to the function equation.
i. (0, 0) ii. (40, 8) iii. (30, 150) iv. (7, 35)

II. For each function equation, use substitution to determine whether the given ordered pairs are solutions.

1. $h(t) = -t^2 + 200$ i. (5, 175) ii. (200, 0) iii. $(-10, 300)$

2. $-4500 + 50d = N(d)$ i. $(-5, -4750)$ ii. $(-4500, 0)$ iii. (90, 0)

3. $C(w) = 2^w$ i. $C(3) = 8$ ii. $32 = C(5)$ iii. $C(0) = 1$

4. $P(n) = -10n + 3000$ i. $P(-3) = 2970$ ii. $P(100) = 2000$ iii. $2800 = P(20)$

III. For each function equation, find the initial value and choose at least 3 other input values to substitute into the equation to find ordered pair solutions. Then write the ordered pairs in function notation and enter the ordered pairs in the table.

1. $D(x) = 2x$

Number x	Double the number $D(x)$

2. $P(n) = -2400 + 20n$

Number of items sold n	Profit from selling n items (\$) $P(n)$

3. $H(t) = -16t^2 + 10t + 5$

Time since release of object (sec.) t	Height of object (ft.) $h(t)$

1.4.B. Modeling a Draining Tank

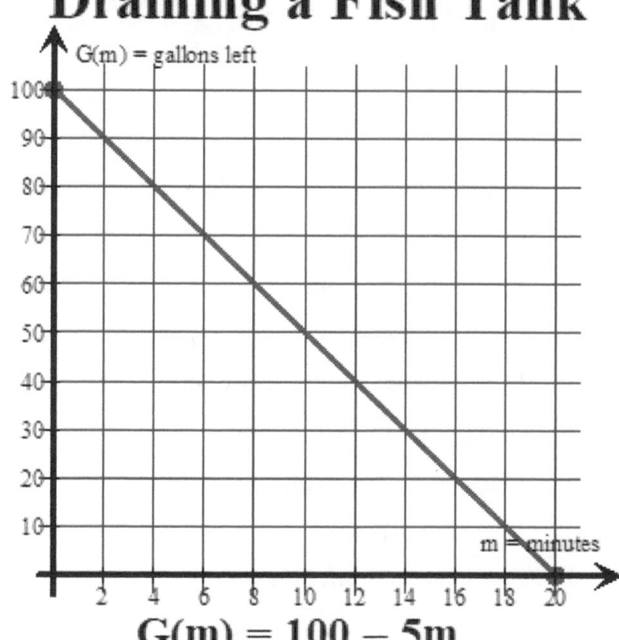

When draining a fish tank, the amount of water left depends on how much time the tank has been draining. Let

IV: m = amount of draining time (minutes)

DV: $G(m)$ = amount of water left after m minutes (gallons).

The relationship between the variables is given by the equation: $\boldsymbol{G(m) = 100 - 5m}$, and the graph of its ordered pair solutions $(\boldsymbol{m}, \boldsymbol{G(m)})$ is shown on the right.

a) Are the variables continuous or discrete? Explain.

b) Identify the real-world domain and range of the function.

- Use points on the graph to answer to each question below. Make estimates when necessary.
- Write the ordered pair from the graph from which you find each answer. Write it also in function notation.
- Substitute the ordered pairs you use to answer questions into the function equation to verify that they are solutions.

c) How much water is in the tank after 6 minutes of draining?

d) After how many minutes of draining will there be 40 gallons left in the tank?

e) Find $G(5)$ and explain its meaning in the context of the situation.

f) Find m when $G(m) = 35$ and interpret its meaning in the context of the situation.

g) After how many minutes will the tank be completely drained?

h) How much water was in the tank when the draining started?

1.4 Concepts and Vocabulary

I. Explain the meaning of each term in your own words.

a) Relation

b) Function

c) Independent variable, Dependent variable

d) Ordered Pair

e) Function Notation

f) Continuous variable versus Discrete variable

g) Domain and Range of a function

h) Initial value of a function

i) Horizontal intercept, Vertical intercept

j) Function Equation

k) Solution to a function equation

II. Using the Profit model (function) represented in various forms below.

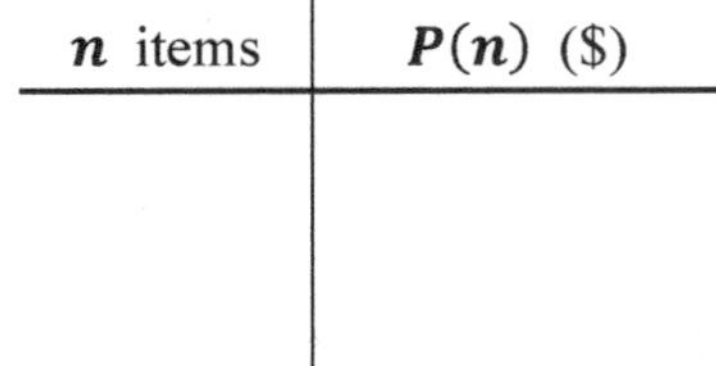

n items	$P(n)$ ($)

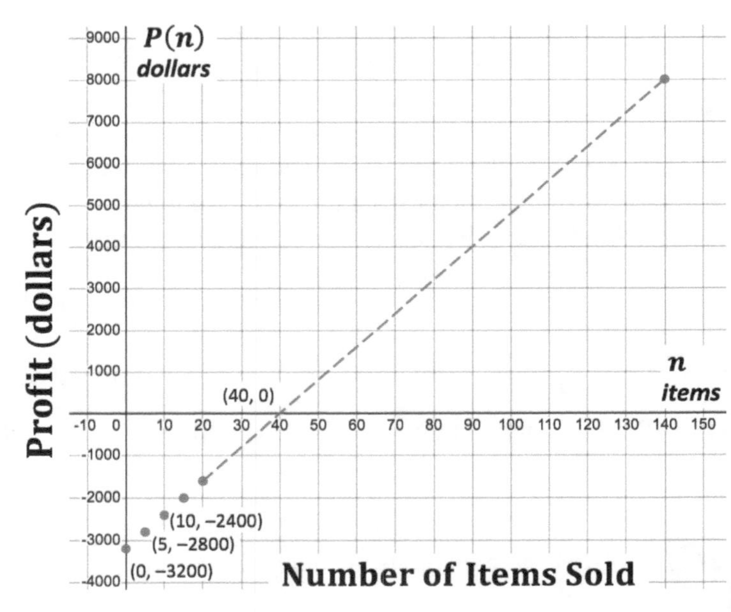

Identify each item listed below for the profit function at right. When appropriate, label the items on the graph, and use the space below to explain its meaning in context.

a) dependent variable

b) independent variable

c) domain

d) range

e) n-intercept

f) $P(n)$-intercept

g) Initial value

h) n -axis

i) $P(n)$-axis

Unit 2 Linear Functions

2.1 Linear Relationships

2.1 Launch: Growing Plants

Half of the class can work on this page and half on the next page. Then compare findings.

I. *Linda bought a 1-foot plant that will grow 4 inches every 3 weeks for the first 15 weeks.*

a) Identify and label the variables.

IV:

DV:

0 weeks 6 weeks 12 weeks

b) Make a table of values. Choose easy ordered pairs. Then examine the table for a pattern.

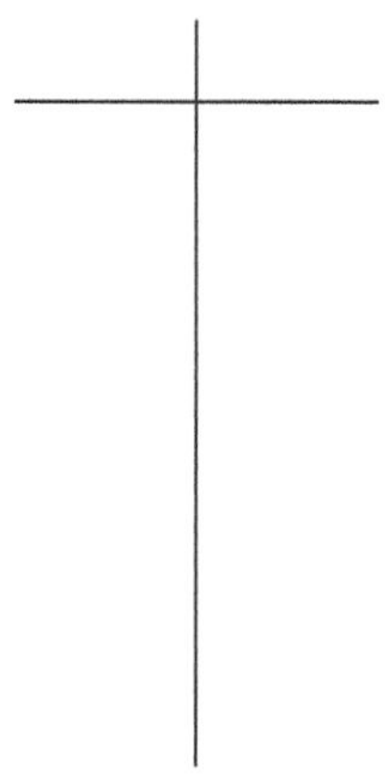

c) Identify the real-world domain and range.

Domain =

Range =

d) Create a graph for the function on the next page.

Compare your plant-height function with the other group's function. Plot their graph on the same grid as yours. Does Linda's or Cheryl's plant grow faster? Explain how you know.

Summarize the main ideas from today's launch. .

II. *Cheryl bought a 1-foot plant that will grow 5 inches every 4 weeks for the first 16 weeks.*

a) Identify and label the variables.

IV:

DV:

b) Make a table of values. Choose easy ordered pairs. Then examine the table for a pattern.

e) Identify the real-world domain and range.

Domain =

Range =

f) Create a graph for the function on the grid..

Compare your plant-height function with the other group's function. Plot their graph on the same grid as yours. Does Linda's or Cheryl's plant grow faster? Explain how you know.

Summarize the main ideas from today's launch.

2.1 Linear Tables

For each table: Determine whether or not it is linear. Show calculations to justify your answer.
If the table is linear, a) identify the constant rate of change *including units*. Is the function increasing or decreasing?
b) If the table is linear, find the initial value and then write the function equation.

1.

t (months)	*P(t)* ($)
3	28,000
7	21,000
11	14,000
15	7,000

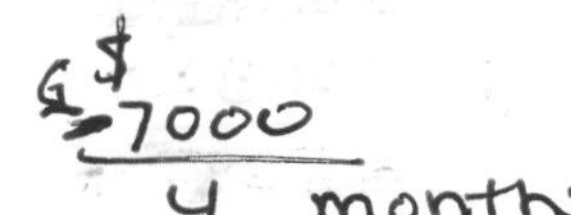

2.

d (days)	*N(d)* (cells)
1	24,000
4	30,000
7	36,000
10	43,000

3.

d (inches) diameter	*C(d)* (inches) circumference
17	53.38
20	62.80
32	100.48
55	172.70

4.

n books sold	***A(n)*** total raised $
0	250
2	264
4	278
6	292
8	306

5.

n toppings	***C(n)*** total cost ($)
0	7.50
2	8.00
4	8.50
6	9.00
10	10.00

6.

t time reading (hrs.)	***P(t)*** pages left to read
3	275
5	175
5.5	150
7	75

2.1 Linear Function Equations

I. Write the formula for a linear function equation. Explain the meaning of the constants $\boldsymbol{m}$ and $\boldsymbol{b}$. You may use the example of growing plants to show how this equation arises inductively.

$y = mx + b$

$m = \text{slope} = \frac{y_2 - y_1}{x_2 - x_1}$

b= inital value

Y int = (0, b)

II. For each equation below, determine whether or not it is a linear function and explain why. IF it is linear, identify the constant rate of change, $\boldsymbol{m}$, and the initial value, $\boldsymbol{b}$. Is it increasing or decreasing?

1. $y = 43x + 7$

slope = 43

intital value = 7

2. $f(x) = 3 - 2x$

$f(x) = -2x + 3$

slope = -2

intial value = 3

3. $h(s) = -40$

4. $C(x) = 2(.06)^x$

Not linear

5. $y = 7x^2 - 8$

6. $V(t) = t$

7. $r(t) = 64t$

8. $k(x) = 32x - 4$

9. $V(r) = 1 - r + r^3$

10. $x = 3$

2.1 Linear Situations

For each linear situation, perform the quantitative analysis, identify the linear constants, and write the equation.

1. *Linda bought a seedling plant that is two feet tall and will grow about ¼ inch per week for 1 year.*

IV:

DV:

Domain:

Range:

Initial value: Constant rate of change:

Function Equation:

Graph: [Section 2.2]

2. *A car rental company charges $25 to rent and 2 cents for every mile driven up to 1400 miles.*

IV: miles m

DV: cost to rent $

Domain: {0, 1, 2 ... 1400} miles

Range: {25, 25.02, 25.04 ... 53} dollars $

Initial value: (0, 25) Constant rate of change: $m = \frac{102}{1}$

Function Equation: $y = mx + b$

$y = 102x + 25$

Graph: [Section 2.2]

$C(m) = 102m + 25$

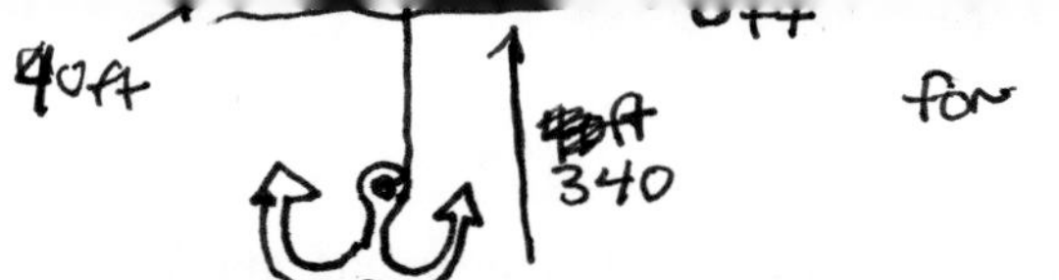

3. *An anchor is lifted up to the deck of a ship which is 40 feet above the water. It is lifted 30 inches per second from a depth of 340 feet below the surface of the ocean. The surface is at sea-level – a depth of zero feet.*

IV: Time

DV: Height

Domain: [0 , 152] seconds

Range: [-340 , 40] feet

Initial value: (0, -340)

Constant rate of change: 2.5 feet per sec = m

Function Equation: y = mx + b

H(t) = 2.5t − 340

Graph: [Section 2.2]

T	H(t)

4. *A sales person earns $450 each week plus 12% commission on her sales up to $50,000 in sales.*

IV:

DV: Paycheck

Domain: {0, .1, .2 … 50000}

Range: {450 … 6000}

Initial value:

Constant rate of change:

Function Equation:

Graph: [Section 2.2]

5. *A new business opens with $40,000 of debt (negative profit) and loses $750 every month for the first two years.*

IV: every month = M

DV: amount of profit $ (P(n))

Domain: {0, 1, 2, . . . 24}

Range: {-40,000, -40,750, -41,500 -58,000}

Initial value: -40,000 (0, -40,000)   Constant rate of change: -750/1

Function Equation: M(P) = -750/1 mon -40,000

Graph: [Section 2.2]

P(N) = -750n - 40,000

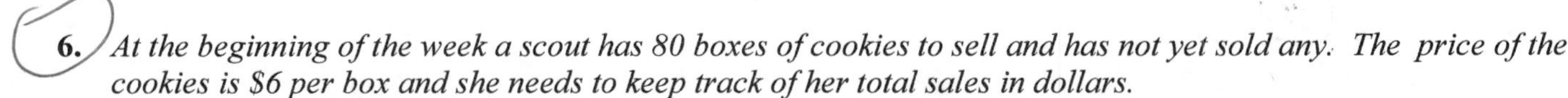

6. *At the beginning of the week a scout has 80 boxes of cookies to sell and has not yet sold any. The price of the cookies is $6 per box and she needs to keep track of her total sales in dollars.*

[2pts]

IV: # of boxes of cookies = n

DV: Sales in dollars = S(n)

Domain: {0, 1, 2 . . . 80} # of boxes sold

Range: {0, 6, 12 . . . 480} Sales $

Initial value: (b = 0, 0)   Constant rate of change: 6/1

Function Equation: S(n) = mn + b

Graph: [Section 2.2]

S(n) = mn + 0

$6 / 1 box

S(n) = 6n + 0

S(n) = 6n

7. *A pool started with 30,000 gallons of water in it and then was drained 12 gallons every 3 minutes. Define the variables 2 different ways to get two different models – one increasing and one decreasing.*

I. As an *Increasing* Model

IV:

DV:

Domain:

Range:

Initial value: Constant rate of change:

Function Equation:

Graph: [Section 2.2]

A pool started with 30,000 gallons of water in it and then was drained 12 gallons every 3 minutes. Define the variables 2 different ways to get two different models – one increasing and one decreasing.

II. As a *Decreasing* Model

IV:

DV:

Domain:

Range:

Initial value: Constant rate of change:

Function Equation:

Graph: [Section 2.2]

2.1 More Tables and Situations

I. For each table:

- Verify that it is linear.
- Find the constant rate of change and the initial value, including units.
- Write the function equation.
- [Section 2.2] Sketch a graph of the function.

1.

n books sold	*A(n)* total raised ($)
0	250
1	262
2	274
3	286
4	298

2.

m miles	*C(m)* total cost of ride ($)
0	0
1	2.25
2	4.50
3	6.75
4	9.00

3.

s side length (m)	*P(s)* Perimeter of a regular polygon (m)
0	0
5	35
10	70
15	105
20	140

4.

s time (second)	*M(s)* megabits
20	5,200
40	10,400
60	15,600
80	20,800

5.

m miles driven	*G(m)* gas left (gallon)
12	14.7
20	14.5
50	13.75
400	5.0

6.

w time (week)	*A(w)* amount in account ($)
22	18,240
30	15,200
38	12,160
60	3,800

II. For each situation:

- Identify and label the independent and dependent variables.
- Verify that the relationship between the variables is linear. Is it increasing or decreasing?
- Find the constant rate of change and the initial value, including units.
- Write the function equation. Check that your equation matches the trend of the function.
- [Section 2.2] Sketch a graph of the function.

1. A yoga studio charges $240 for the year and $5 per class.

2. A diver rose towards the surface of the water 30 feet each minute from a depth of 390 feet below the surface.

3. A plane was cruising at an altitude of 10,400 feet and then starts to descend 400 feet every minute.

4. A new business opens with a debt of $3400 and loses another $400 every month for the first year.

5. A pizza place charges $9 for a small cheese pizza and another 95 cents per topping.

6. The flood waters were 5 feet deep and then every day the water receded 9 inches.

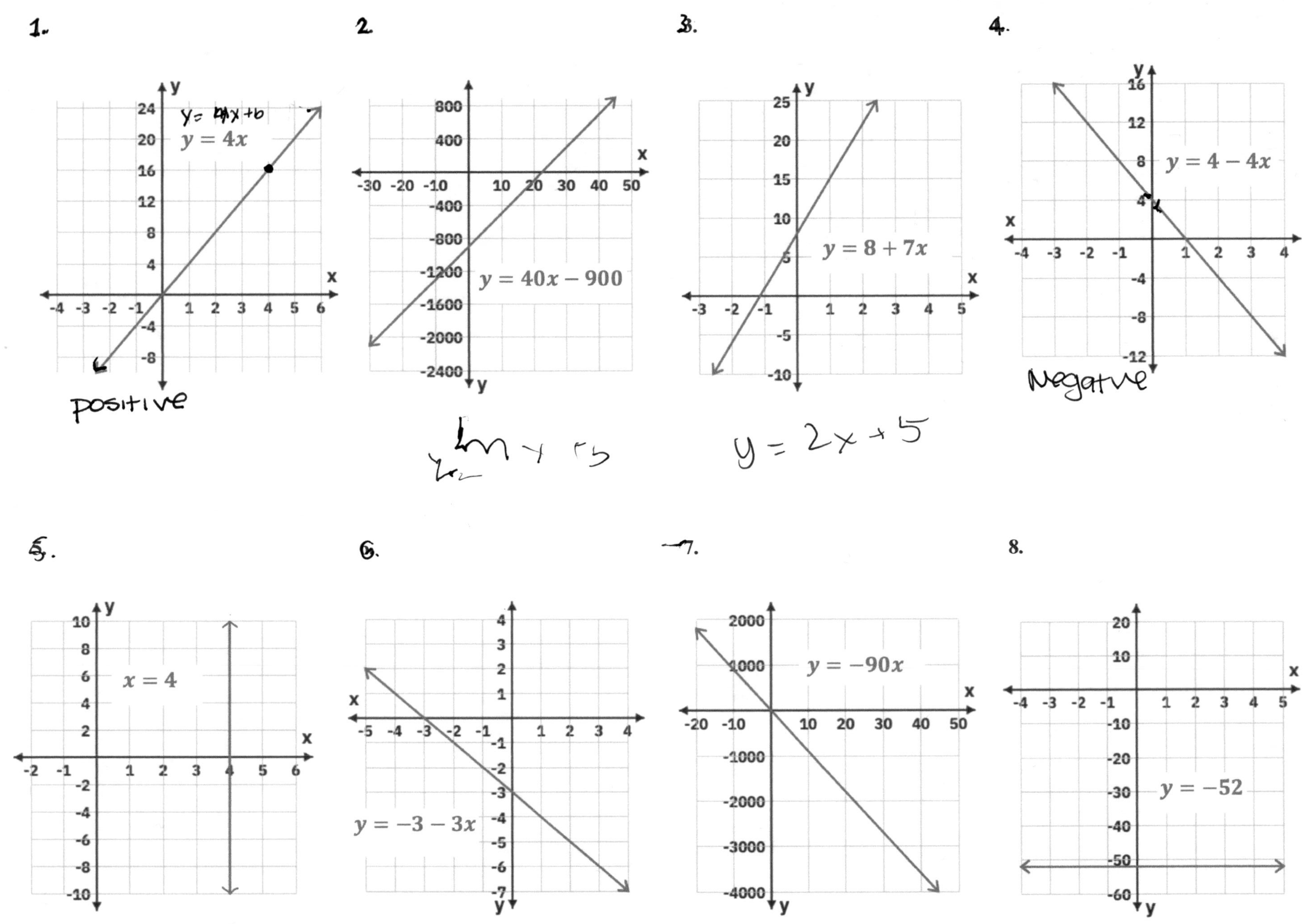
1.
$y = 4x$
2.
$y = 40x - 900$
3.
$y = 8 + 7x$
4.
$y = 4 - 4x$
5.
$x = 4$
6.
$y = -3 - 3x$
7.
$y = -90x$
8.
$y = -52$

2.2 Analyzing Linear Functions

2.2 Launch: Exploring Linear Graphs

Work in pairs.
For the graphs on the opposite page, fill in the table on the right and then answer the questions below.

Mark and label intercepts on the graphs.

Equation	m	b	Direction	*y*-intercept	*x*-intercept

a) What do the equations for the increasing graphs have in common? Decreasing graphs?

b) Which graph of a function is neither increasing nor decreasing? What kind of function is it?

y=mx+b

y=4x+-2

c) Do all the graphs have a y-intercept? Explain. Do they all have x-intercepts? If yes, how many?

d) Which graph is not the graph of a function? Explain.

e) Summarize your findings – what connections among the concepts in the columns did you find?

2.2 Linear Graphs

I. Go back to Linear Situations (1) – (7) in section 2.1 and sketch graphs for those function equations.

II. *Sketch* a graph for each of the following functions on their given domain. Label the vertical intercept.

a) $A(t) = -600 + 50t$ on domain $\{0, 1, 2, \ldots, 20\}$

b) $P(n) = -100tn + 1500$ on domain $[0, 30]$

c) $H(w) = 14 + \frac{1}{2}w$ on domain $[0, 100]$

d) $L(t) = -2{,}000$ on domain $\{0, 5, 10, \ldots, 365\}$

III. For each linear graph, write an equation with *numerical* coefficients $\boldsymbol{m}$ and $\boldsymbol{b}$ that could represent it.

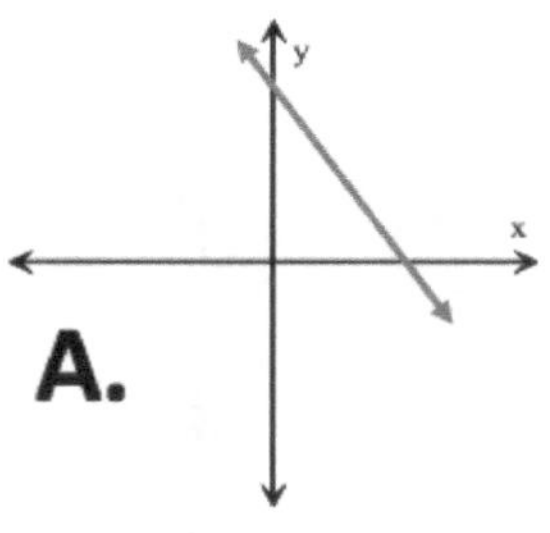

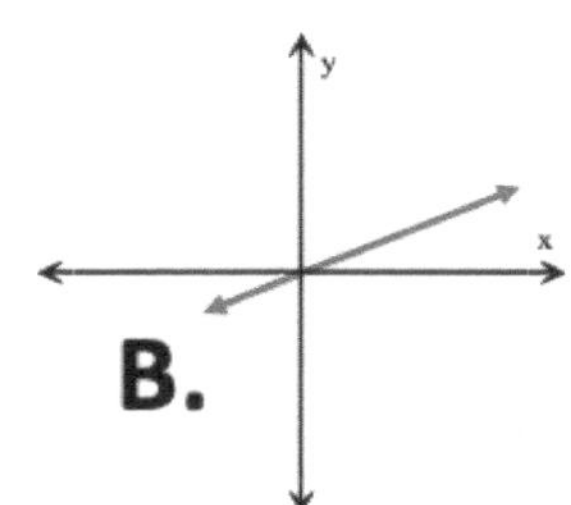

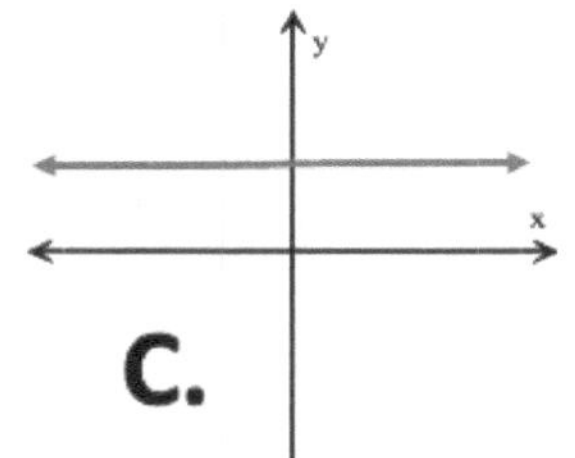

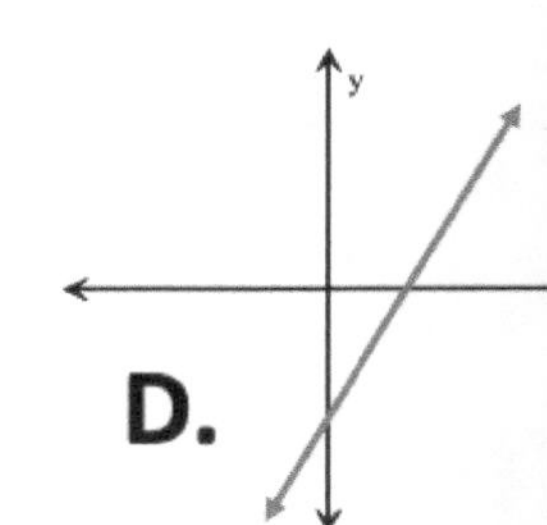

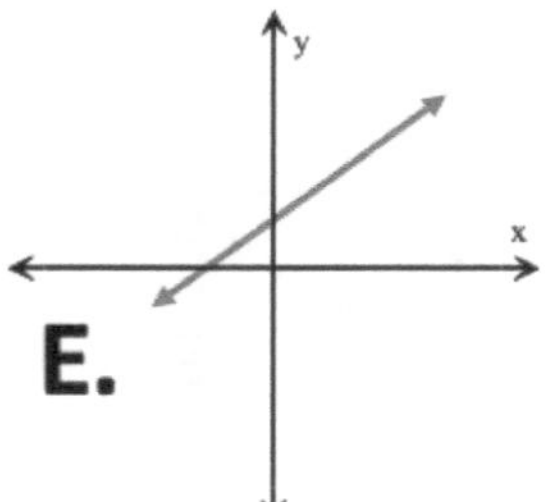

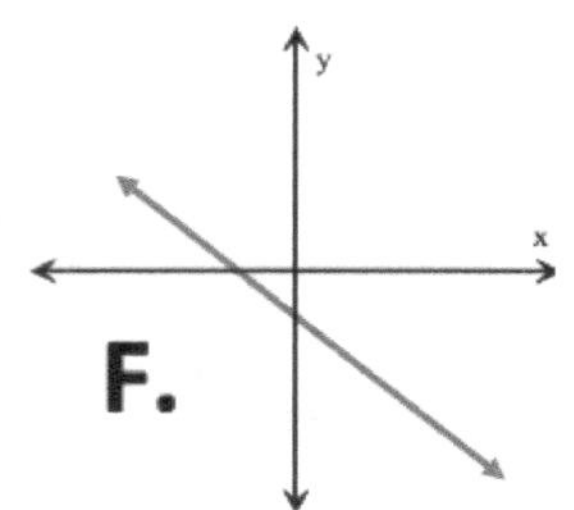

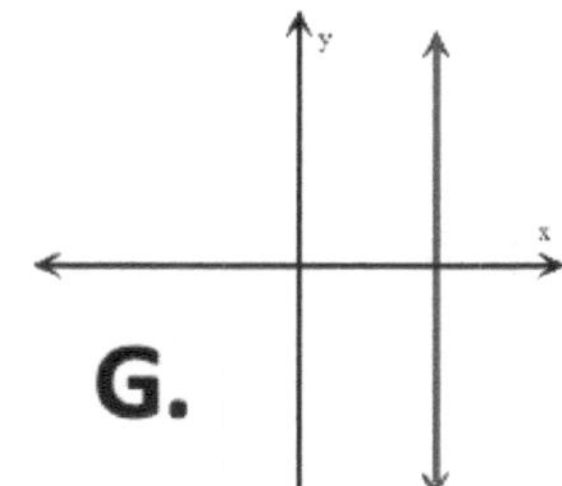

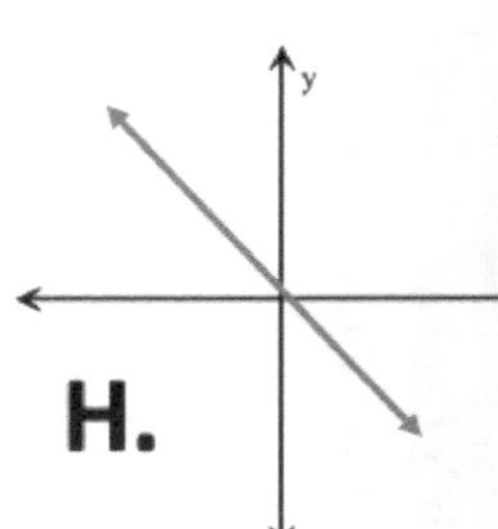

2.2 Writing Linear Equations from Graphs

For each graph:

a) Write the practical domain and range for the graph. You may have to use the equation to find an endpoint.
b) Find the slope and *explain what it means* with units. Use *lattice* or *marked* points and show work.
c) Identify or find the *exact* initial value (vertical intercept) and write an equation for the linear function.
d) Use the equation to find the horizontal intercept. Label it and explain its practical meaning or why it has none.

1. Domain:

Range::

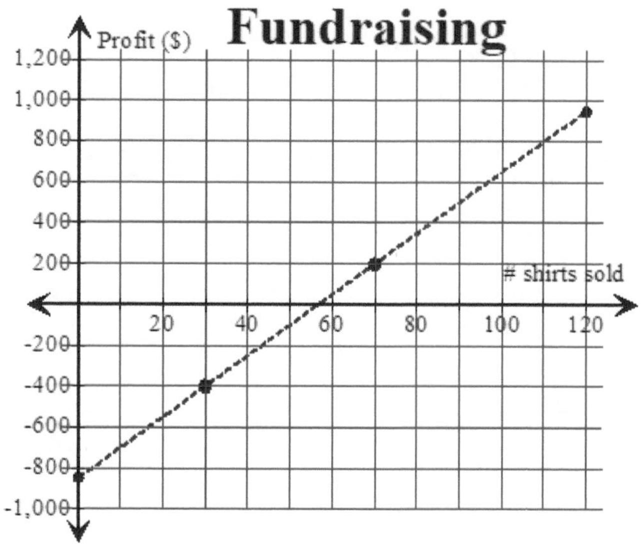

Fundraising

Profit ($)

1,200
1,000
800
600
400
200
-200
-400
-600
-800
-1,000

20 40 60 80 100 120

shirts sold

Slope (CRCh):

Vertical intercept (initial value):

Equation:

Horizontal intercept:

2. Domain:

Range::

Slope (CRCh):

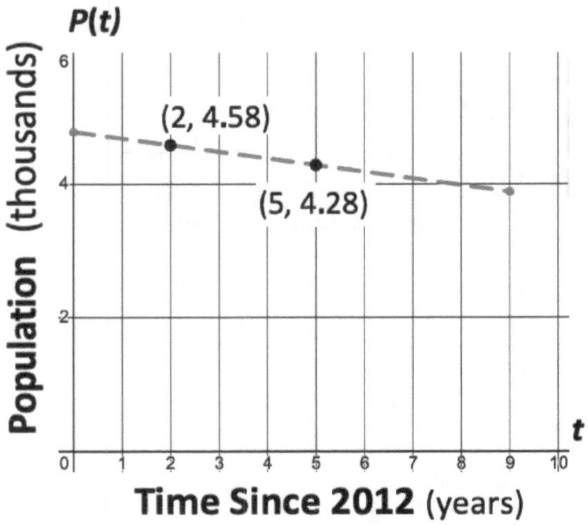

Vertical intercept
(initial value):

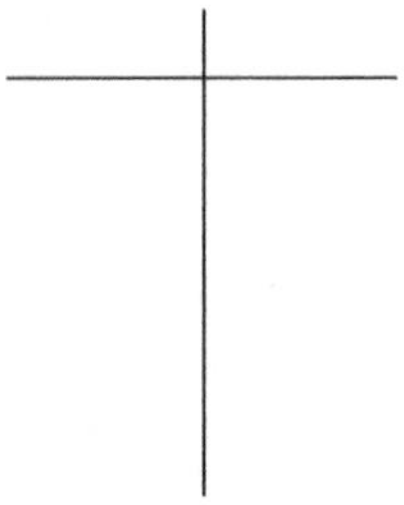

Equation:

Horizontal intercept:

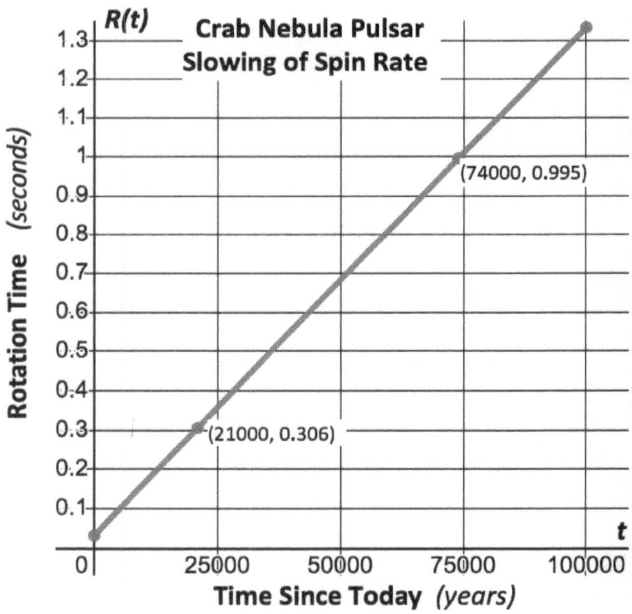

3. Domain:

Range::

Slope (CRCh):

Vertical intercept:

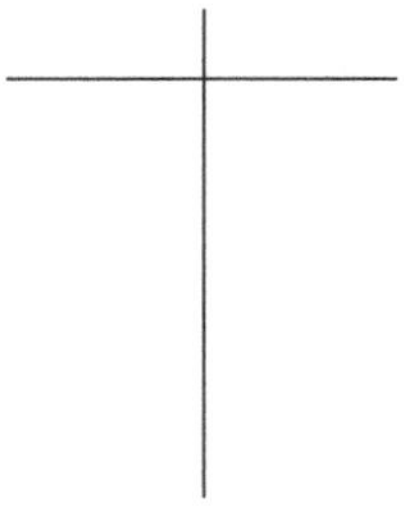

Equation:

Horizontal intercept:

4. Domain:

Range::

Slope:

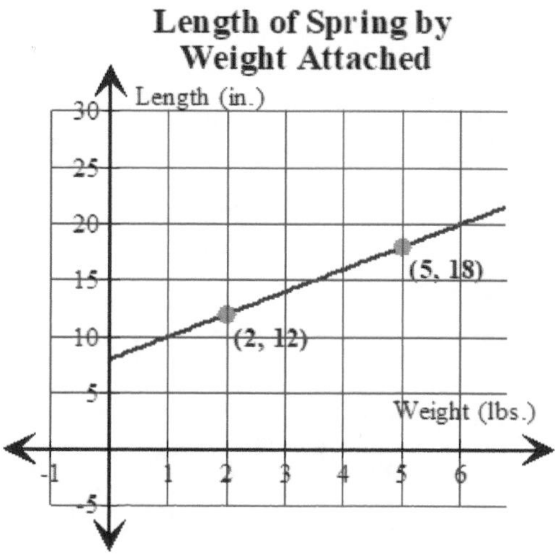
Length of Spring by Weight Attached
Length (in.)
Weight (lbs.)
(2, 12)
(5, 18)
30
25
20
15
10
5
-5
-1
1
2
3
4
5
6

Vertical intercept:

Equation:

Horizontal intercept:

5. Domain:

Range::

Slope:

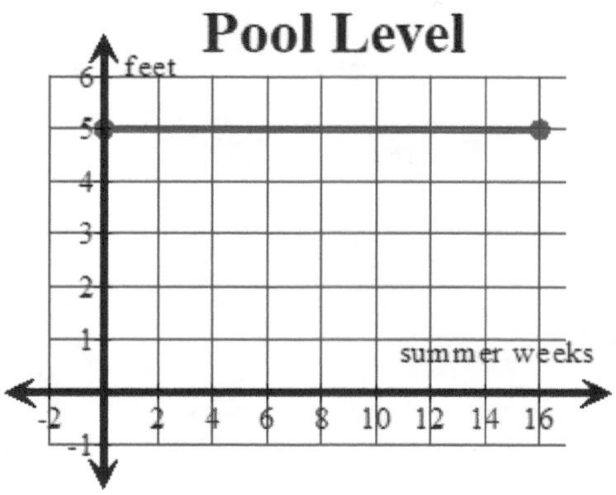
Pool Level
feet
summer weeks
6
5
4
3
2
1
-1
-2
2
4
6
8
10
12
14
16

Vertical intercept:

Equation:

Horizontal intercept:

6. Domain:

Range::

Slope:

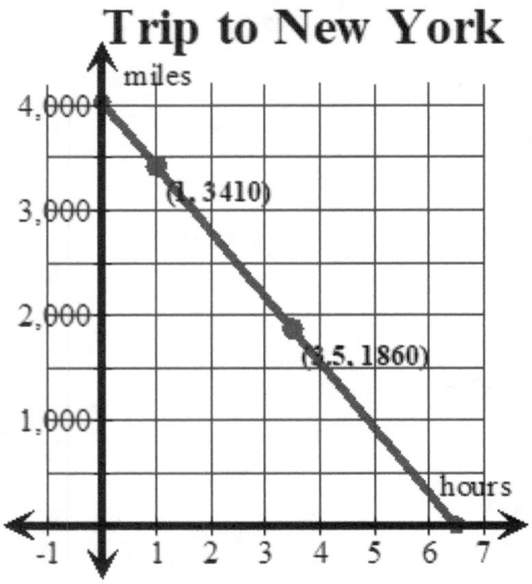

Vertical intercept:

Equation:

Horizontal intercept:

7. Domain:

Range::

Slope:

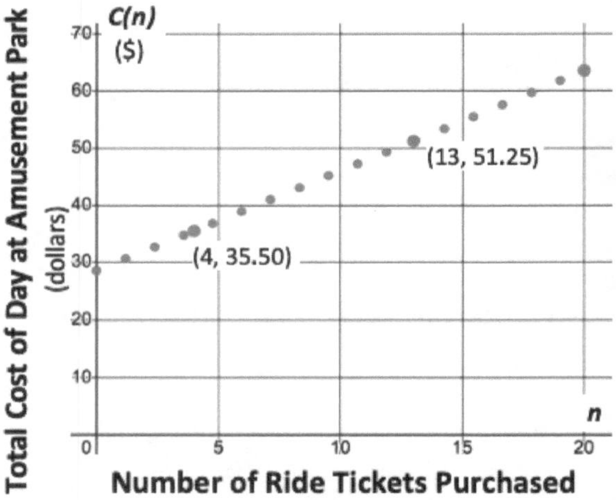

Vertical intercept:

Equation:

Horizontal intercept:

2.2 Writing Linear Equations from Tables

I. Go back to Linear Function Tables (1) – (6) and More Linear Tables (1) – (6) in section 2.1 and write the equations for the tables that are linear.

II. For each table below, verify that it is linear. Show the calculations to justify your answer.
If the table is linear then

a) Identify the slope (constant rate of change) and the vertical intercept (initial value) *including units*.
b) Write an equation for the linear function.
c) Use your equation to find the horizontal intercept. Write it in function notation and explain its meaning or why it has none.

1. Linear?

Slope:

t time a candle burns (hours)	$H(t)$ height of the candle (cm)
0	24
2	21
4	18
8	12

Vertical intercept:

Equation:

Horizontal intercept:

2. Linear?

Slope:

t = Time Traveled (hrs.)	$D(t)$ = Distance Driven (km.)
2	220
3	320
4	420
7.5	770

Vertical intercept:

Equation:

Horizontal intercept:

3. Linear?

$t =$ Time Traveled (min.)	$D(t) =$ Distance Left (mi.)
36	273
52	261
88	234
268	99

Slope:

Vertical intercept:

Equation:

Horizontal intercept:

4. Linear?

$h =$ number of fundraising hats sold	$P(h) =$ profit earned from h hats sold ($)
80	– 980
115	– 490
170	280
245	1330

Slope:

Vertical intercept:

Equation:

Horizontal intercept:

5. Linear?

Slope:

Vertical intercept:

Equation:

Horizontal intercept:

t = time since 5pm (hours)	$H(t)$ = height of the candle (inch)
0.5	8
1	8
5	8
1	8

6. Linear?

Slope:

Vertical intercept:

Equation:

Horizontal intercept:

t = time on elevator ride (seconds)	H(t) = height above ground (ft.)
2	192
5	120
7	72

2.2 Comparing Cars

For each diagram, answer the following questions. JUSTIFY your reasoning with calculations .

a) Which car is the fastest?
b) Which car is the slowest?
c) Which car is parked?

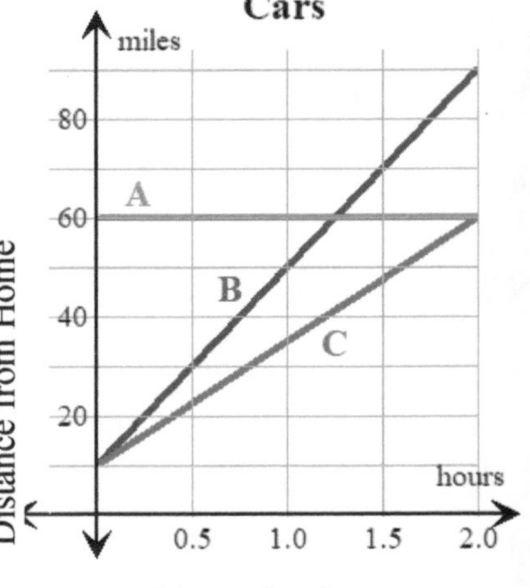

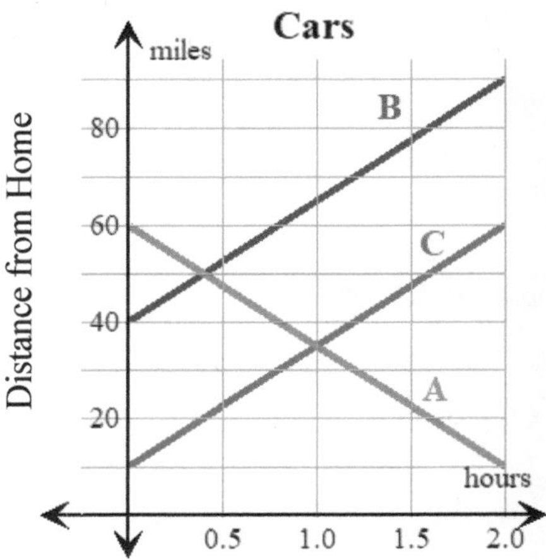

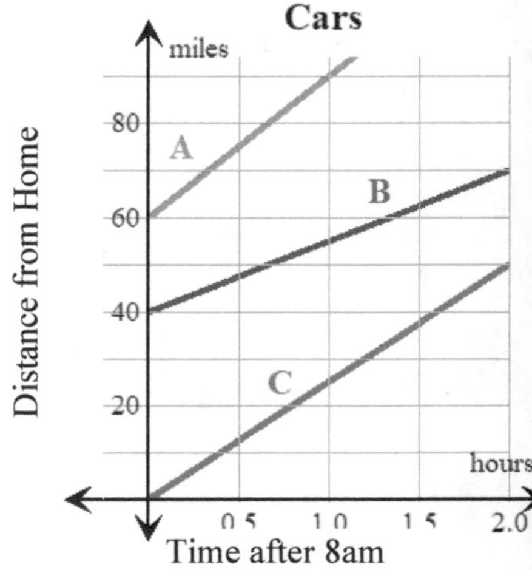

2.2 Slope Clinic

Slope m of a line $y = mx + b$:

- represents the **constant rate of change** of a linear function whose graph is that line.
- gives the **steepness and direction of the graph** of a linear function.
- is the ratio rise over run between any two points (x_1, y_1) and (x_2, y_2) on that line.

$$m = \frac{\Delta y}{\Delta x} = \frac{\textit{Change in 2 Outputs}}{\textit{Change in their 2 Inputs}} = \frac{y_2 - y_1}{x_2 - x_1} = \frac{\textit{Rise}}{\textit{Run}}$$

- The **slope m** of a line can be found from a graph using slope triangles.

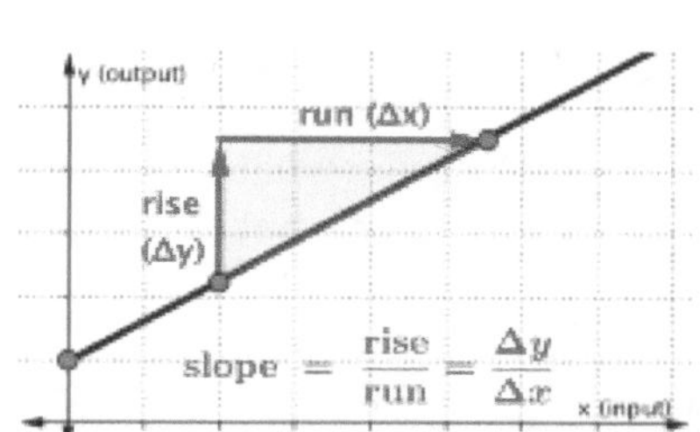

Figure 2.6 Slope Triangle

Determine the slope of each line below.

a)

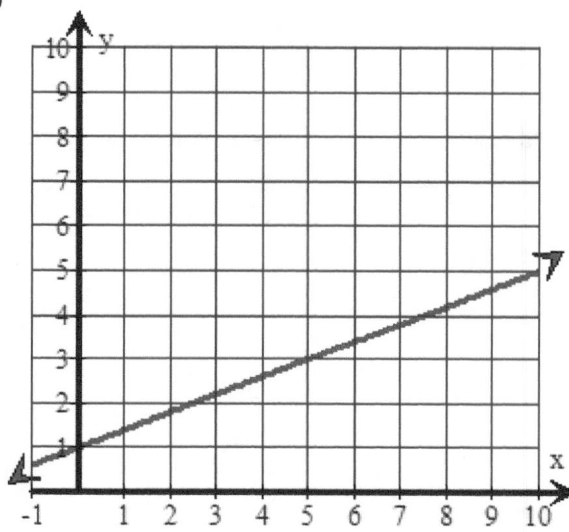

b)

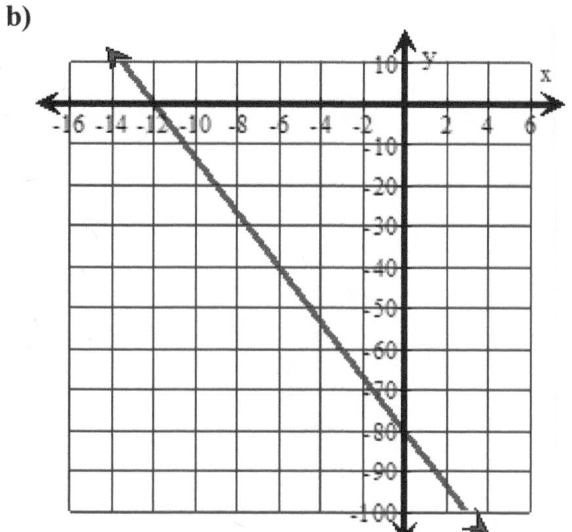

2.2 Intercepts Clinic

1. Describe what a **vertical intercept** of a graph is and how to find it algebraically from a function equation. What other names do we use for the vertical intercept?

2. Describe what a **horizontal intercept** of a graph is and how to find it algebraically from a function equation. What other names do we use for the horizontal intercept?

3. Find the vertical and horizontal intercepts of each function algebraically. Label which is which and write the ordered pair in function notation.

a) $N(x) = 90x - \frac{1}{2}$ b) $G(n) = -340 - 4n$ c) $L(t) = 12t^2 - 450$

2.3 Linear Modeling

2.3 Launch: Window Washers

Window washers begin to lower the platform down the side of a building. The function $\boldsymbol{h(t) = 168 - \frac{1}{2}t}$ *gives the height in feet off of the ground of the platform* $\boldsymbol{t}$ *seconds after they began to lower it down.*

1. Identify which is the independent and which is the dependent variable.

IV:

DV:

2. Explain the meaning of the constants 168 and $-\frac{1}{2}$ in the equation, including units.

3. Use the function equation to answer the following questions. Express each answer in function notation and enter it in the table as an ordered pair.

a) How tall is the building?

b) How high off the ground is the platform after one minute?

c) How long will it take them to reach the ground?

d) Write the domain and range of the model.

e) Sketch the graph of the function. Identify, label, and interpret the t-intercept and the $h(t)$-intercept.

2.3 Creating and Using Linear Models

1. *Sam repairs cars and gets paid in 15-minute increments. For jobs up to 8 hours, there is a linear relationship between the amount of time the repair takes and the total cost of the job. Sasha paid Sam \$260 for a repair that took 90 minutes. Paolo paid Sam \$440 for a repair that took 3 hours.*

a) Suppose we want to know how much a 2-hour repair would cost. Do we have enough information to find the answer to this question? Why or why not?

b) What does it mean when we say that there is a "linear relationship" between two quantities?

c) Which quantity is the independent variable and which is the dependent variable in this situation?

IV:

DV:

d) Write a linear equation relating the two variables.

e) Can you use the equation to find the cost of a 2-hour repair? If so, do it.

f) If a repair cost \$920, how much time did the repair take? Use substitution with the function equation.

In section 1.5 we said that a function equation could be used as a *model* for a real world situation. If the equation is linear we call it a *linear model.*

g) Give examples of at least two other questions that we can ask about the Repair-Jobs situation and answer using the linear model. Then show how to find those answers.

h) Give an example of a question about the variables that we cannot answer using this linear model.

i) What are the domain and range of the model? Explain.

f) Sketch the graph of the function. Identify, label, and interpret the intercepts.

2. A group of people took an elevator ride in a building that stands 280 feet tall. They rode up to the 12th floor which is 210 feet above the ground. The table at right shows the elevator's height with respect to the ground during the ride.

t = time on elevator (seconds)	$H(t)$ = height (feet)
4.5	5.25
7	31.5
12	84

a) Label and describe independent and dependent variables including units.

IV: time

DV: height

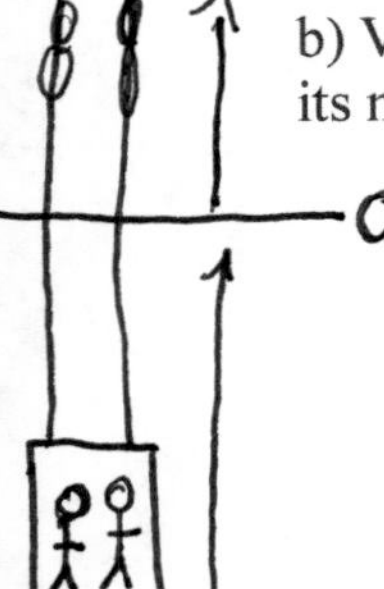

b) Verify that the table is linear and calculate the constant rate of change. Interpret its meaning in context including units. Show your work.

yes it is linear.

per every 4.5 secs it travels 5.25 ft

h(t) = 10.5 (t) +

c) Find the initial value using substitution. Interpret its meaning in context including units. Show work.

d) Write the function equation using appropriate variables.

e) Write the real-world domain and range. Show calculations to find endpoints.

f) Sketch a graph of the function.
Identify and label intercepts.

g) Use substitution to find the elevator's height above ground after 9 seconds.

h) Use substitution to find out how long will it take to reach 115.5 feet above ground.

3. *After a hurricane in Springfield, there was 6 feet of water covering Main Street. Each day after the hurricane the water level went down by 6 inches.*

a) Label and describe independent and dependent variables including units.

IV:

DV:

b) Explain how you know this is a linear situation.

c) Identify the constants including units – the constant rate of change and the initial value.

d) Write the function equation.

e) Write the real-world domain and range. Show calculations to find endpoints.

f) Sketch a graph of the function.

g) How long after the hurricane were there only 4 ½ feet of water? Use substitution.

h) How deep was the flood water after 54 hours?

i) How deep was the water after 2 weeks?

4. *There is a linear relationship between the total cost of a renting a van from the Wrecks-R-Us Company and the number of miles the van is driven. Steve rented a van and paid $42.50 for driving 50 miles. Gabriella paid $53 for driving 120 miles.*

IV:

DV:

Write the linear equation that models this situation: Show and label all calculations.

Domain =

Range =

a) How much would it cost to rent a van if you drive 75 miles?

b) How far did Shay drive the van if it cost her a total of $99.80?

c) Sketch the graph of the total cost function.

5. *The linear graph on the right describes a linear situation.*

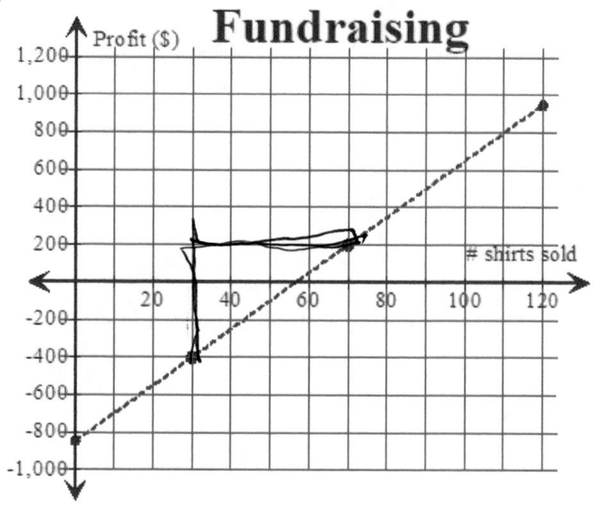

IV:

DV:

Write the linear equation that models this situation:
Show and label all calculations.

Fundraising

Profit ($)

1,200 1,000 800 600 400 200 -200 -400 -600 -800 -1,000

shirts sold

20 40 60 80 100 120

Domain =

Range =

a) Find the *exact* 'x'-intercept. Rename this intercept using your variables. Describe its meaning in context.

b) Find the *exact* 'y'-intercept. Rename this intercept using your variables. Interpret its contextual meaning.

c) Exactly how many shirts did they sell if the profit is $575?

d) Exactly how much profit do they earn if they sell 113 shirts?

2.3 Critical Thinking

1. *In 2012 the average price of tickets at box offices in the U.S. was \$7.96, and was \$8.65 in 2016. Assume that the average ticket price is a linear function of time from 2012 to 2016.*
   (Hint: Define the independent variable so that the year 2012 is shifted to the initial input, $t = 0$ years.)

IV:

DV:

Write the linear equation that models this situation. Show and label all calculations.

Domain =

Range =

a) Estimate the average ticket price in the 2014.

b) What does this data predict the average ticket price would have been in the year 2017?

c) According to this model, in what year was the average price \$5.89?

d) According to this model, what would have been the average ticket price in 1965?

e) Do you think a linear model for ticket prices over time is valid? Explain/Discuss.

2. *There is a linear relationship between the price a shop charges for a product and the quantity of that product that will sell at that price. If the shop charges \$6 for a t-shirt, they will sell 27 of them that week. If the shop charges \$14 for a t-shirt, they will sell only 3 of them that week.*

Identify and label the independent and dependent variables. Include units.

Are the variables discrete or continuous? Explain.

a) Write a function equation that models the relationship between variables.

b) How many t-shirts will they sell if they charge only \$4.66 for one shirt?

c) Realistically, what is the largest number of shirts they could sell? Explain how you can figure this out and show the *calculations*.

d) What is the highest price they can charge? Explain how you can figure this out and show the *calculations*.

e) Use your answers from (c) and (d) to write the domain and range. Include units!

Self-Assessment Test 2: Modeling and Linear Functions

INSTRUCTIONS: Show all calculations and label all work. Whenever the function equation is available, (is given or you are asked to write it), find answers using substitution into the function equation.

1. a) The table at right shows a relation between first and last names. Explain why the relation is or is not a function. Be specific.

Input	Output
Liz	Campbell
Mel	Smith
Liz	Johnson
Linda	Ramirez
Rich	Ocelli
Peter	Smith

b) Explain why each graph below does or does not represent a function. Be specific!

A.

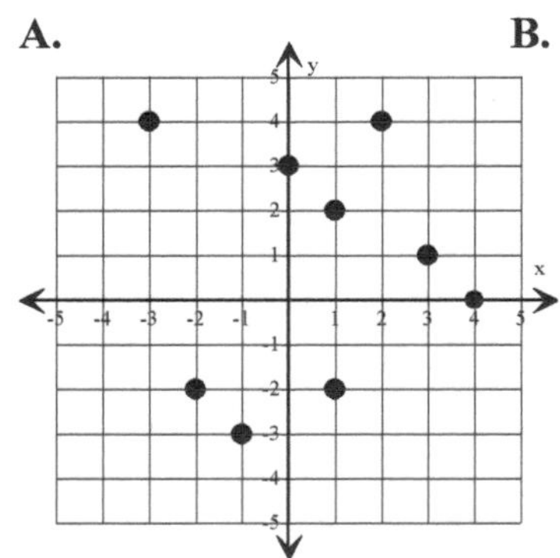

B.

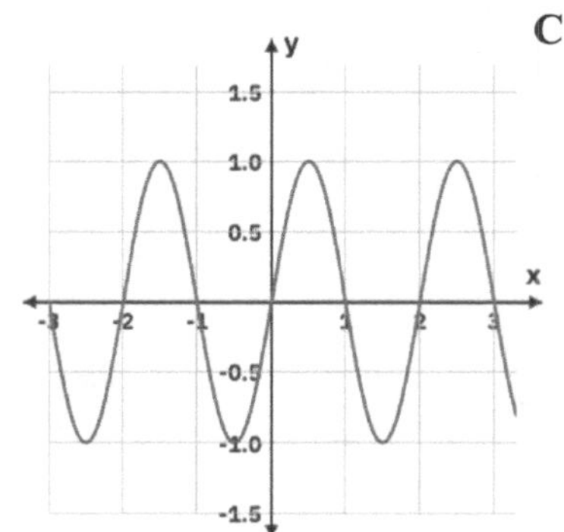

C.

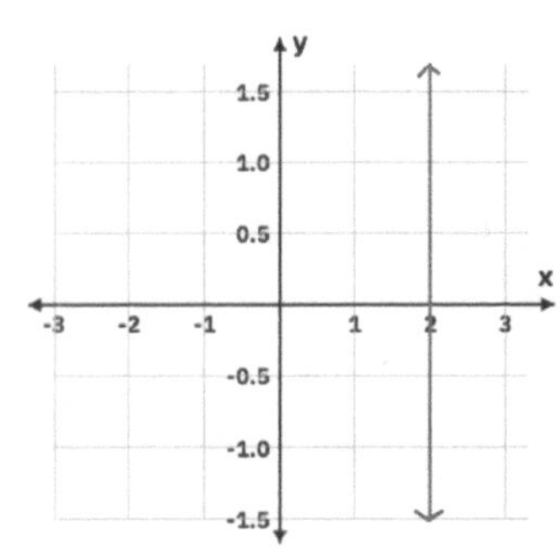

2. *The table shows total amounts charged for an equipment rental and the amount of time it was rented.*

Time (hours) t	Total Cost ($) $C(t)$
13	224
16	266
21	336
30	462

a) Verify that the table is linear and find the constant rate of change including units.

b) Write a function equation that represents the table. Show work.

c) For how much time was the equipment rented if the total charge is $906.50?

3. *A pool is full at a level of 14 feet and is going to be drained for the winter season. The drain removes water that brings down the level 3 inches every hour.*

a) Identify and label the dependent and independent variables in this situation including units.

Are the variables discrete or continuous? Explain.

b) Explain how you know this is a linear situation.

c) Identify the slope of this function. Explain its contextual meaning including units.

d) Write a function equation that models the situation.

e) Find the *exact* 'x'-intercept. Rename it using your variables. Describe its meaning in context.

f) Find the *exact* 'y'-intercept. Rename it using your variables. Interpret its contextual meaning.

g) Give the real-world domain and range of this function including units.

Domain =

Range =

h) Sketch a graph of this function.

4. *There is a linear relationship between the profit a club earns on a fundraiser selling cany bars and the number of candy bars they sell. If they only sell 50 candy bars their profit will be \$–240 (a loss). If they sell 500, their profit will be \$1,110. The club has a total of 2,000 candy bars to sell.*

a) Identify and label the independent and dependent variables. Include units.

Are the variables discrete or continuous? Explain.

b) Write a function equation that models the relationship between variables.

c) How many candy bars did they sell if the profit was \$1,626?

d) How many candy bars must they sell to break-even?

e) Write the domain and range for this club's fundraiser model.

5. *The graph on the right models a money-saving situation.*

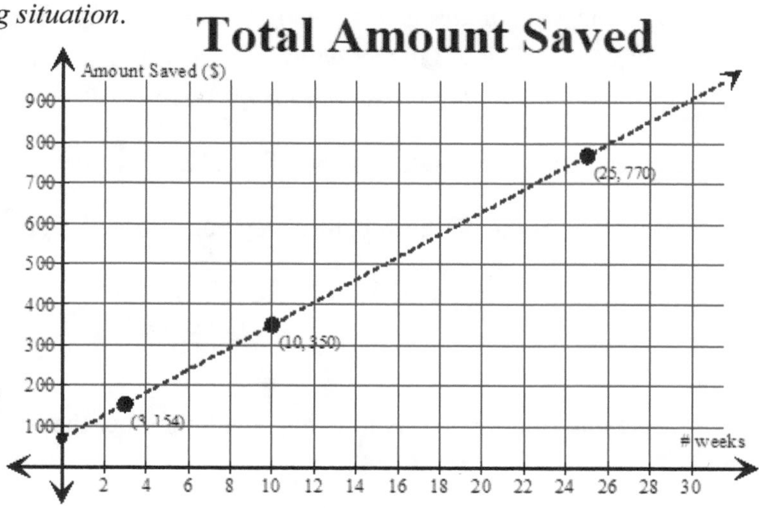

Total Amount Saved

Amount Saved ($)

900, 800, 700, 600, 500, 400, 300, 200, 100

(3, 154) (10, 350) (25, 770)

weeks

2 4 6 8 10 12 14 16 18 20 22 24 26 28 30

a) Identify and choose labels for the variables.

IV:

DV:

Are the variable treated as discrete or continuous? How do you know?

b) Find the slope of the line.

Explain what the slope means in this context. Include units.

c) Find the vertical intercept algebraically. Identify its name using your variables.

Explain the meaning of the vertical intercept in this context. Include units.

d) Write an equation for the graph.

e) How much will have been saved after one year?

f) How long would it take to save $2030?

g) Write the domain and range for this money-saving model.

6. *Window washers are getting ready to work and they begin to hoist the platform up the side of a building to the 10th floor, which is 120 feet above the ground. The function* $\mathbf{h(t)} = \frac{1}{2}\mathbf{t} + \mathbf{3}$ *gives the height in feet off of the ground of the pulley-bucket platform* $\mathbf{t}$ *seconds after they began to pull it up.*

Answer questions completely with units and express them in function notation.

a) How high is the platform before they begin to pull it up?

b) Give one solution to this function equation, other than the answer to (a), and *explain what it means* in context.

c) How high off the ground is the platform after one minute?

d) How long will it take for the platform to reach the 6th floor, which is 72 feet high?

e) If $h(t) = 20$, find the missing value in the ordered pair described by that function notation.

Explain what that ordered pair means in this situation.

f) Give the real world domain and range for this function including units. Show calculations to find endpoints.

g) Graph the function. Label axes and endpoints.

For each problem (7) – (9):

- Perform the Quantitative Analysis (Constants and Variables)
- Express Relations between the Quantities (Write Translations and Related Formulas)
- Solve the System of Equations by Substitution.
- Verify any additional requirements (inequalities) and Check your solution.

7. *Each side of a triangular garden has a different length. The longest side is 4 feet longer than the mid-length side, and the shortest side is 27 inches shorter than the mid-length side. Find the length of each side of the garden if its perimeter is 100 feet.*

8. *A teacher is using ribbon to create an outline on the bulletin board as shown in the figure at right. Each section has the shape of an equilateral triangle. The total area inside the large triangle is 4,330 square centimeters. The altitude (height) of a small triangle is 0.866 times its side length. What is the side length of the small triangles in the pattern? What is the altitude of the small triangles?*

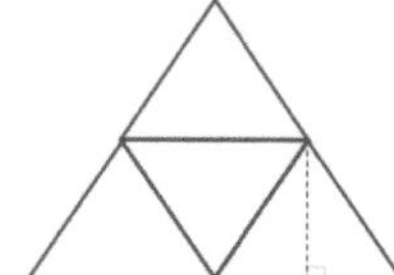

9. *A student spent a total of 3.25 hours studying, then eating lunch, then walking to a friend's house. The time she spent studying was 2 minutes less than four times the time she spent eating lunch. She spent 5 minutes more walking to her friend's house than she did eating lunch. How much time did she spend doing each activity?*

Answer Key Test 2

1. a) The table is NOT a function as the input of Liz has two *different* outputs – Campbell and Johnson.

   b)Graph A is NOT a function as the input of $x = 1$ has two *different* outputs, $y = -2$ and $y = 2$.
   Graph B IS a function. Every input (x-value) has only one output. That many inputs share an output is fine.
   Graph C is NOT a function. ALL the points on a vertical line have only one input but infinitely many outputs.

2. a) To verify that the table is linear, we check the 3 rates of change between sets of consecutively listed points in the table. They all result in the same, constant rate of change; $m = 14$ \$/hr., which means it IS linear.
   b) Next we substitute a point from the table into an almost-complete linear function equation to find the vertical intercept or initial value: $b = 42$ dollars.
   c) Substituting $C(t) = 906.50 = 42 + 14t$, we solve for t to get $t = 61.75$ hours results in a cost of \$906.50.

3. a) IV: t – amount of time draining (hours); DV: $L(t)$ - water level (feet) OR (inches)
   The variables are continuous as the values for water level cannot have gaps – the water level cannot 'skip' over any levels as it drains. It must hit *every* water level between 14 and 0 feet as it drains.
   b) We know it is linear because we recognize a *constant rate of change* between variables: – 3 *inches per hour*.
   c) Slope $m = -1/4$ feet per hour; every hour the water level decreases by ¼ foot, OR $m = -3$ inch per hour
   d) $L(t) = 14 - \frac{1}{4}t$ in feet OR $L(t) = 168 - 3t$ in inches.
   e) The 'x'-intercept is the t-intercept by our labels and we find it by substituting $L(t) = 0$ into the equation. We get $t = 54$, which means it takes 54 hours for the water level to reach 0 feet or inches. $L(54) = 0$.
   f) The 'y'-intercept is the $L(t)$-intercept by our labels and we find it by substituting $t = 0$ into the equation. We get initial value $L(0) = 14$ feet OR $L(0) = 168$ inches. It gives us the water level before draining began.
   g) Domain = [0,56] hours; Range = [0,14] feet OR [0, 168] inches

4. a) IV: n – number of candy bars sold (candy bar); DV: $P(n)$ = profit club earns from selling n candy bars (\$). The variables are discrete. Input values have gaps between whole numbers – you cannot sell a fraction of a candy bar. The output will have gaps as each time a candy bar is sold, the amount of money will skip by the amount they earn from a candy bar. (We'll find out that amount when we find the constant rate of change.)
   b) We put the two given ordered pairs in table and first find the CRCh, $m =$ 3 \$/bar. Using a known ordered pair we sub into nearly completed equation to find $b = -390$. We have $P(n) = -390 + 3n$.
   c) Sub $P(n) = 1626 = -390 + 3n$. They must sell $n = 672$ candy bars. $P(672) = \$1626$
   d) Break even means $P(n)$ =0. Solving $P(n) = 0 = -390 + 3n$, we get $n = 130$ candy bars. $P(130) = \$0$.
   e) First find the endpoint that tells us the profit when the club sells all 2,000 candy bars: $P(2000) = \$5610$.
   Domain = $\{0, 1, 2, \ldots, 2000\}$ candy bars; Range = $\{-390, -387, -384, \ldots, 5610\}$ dollars.

5. a) IV: w – amount of time saving (weeks); DV: $A(w)$ - amount saved after w weeks (\$); The variables are treated as discrete which we can tell by the dotted-line graph. We can imagine that money is deposited into the savings exactly once per week so the times skips by whole weeks and the amount of savings will jump (have gaps) by whatever amount is added each week.
   b) The slope is $m = +28$ \$ per week; Slope is the amount the savings *increases* each week (It's the constant rate of change.);
   c) The vertical intercept is the $A(w)$- intercept by our labels, or the initial value, b, of the linear function. We find it by substituting a known ordered pair from the graph into the equation. We get $b = 70$. At 0 weeks there was \$70 already saved. $A(0\ wks.) = \$70$
   d) $A(w) = 28w + 70$;
   e) Convert 1 year to $w = 52$ weeks, $A(52\ weeks) = \$1526$;
   f) Substitute $A(w)$= $2030 = 70 + 28w$, and solve to get $w = 70$ weeks. $(70\ weeks) = \$2030$
   g) We have no known endpoint for the savings model so we leave it open. Domain = {0, 1, 2, ...} weeks, and Range = {70, 98, 126, ...} dollars.

6. a) 3 feet; b) $(10,8)$ means that the platform is 8 feet above ground in 10 seconds; c) 33 feet; d) 2.3 minutes; e) $t = 34$ seconds; the platform will be 20 feet above the ground in 34 seconds;

f) Domain = [0,234] seconds; Range = [3,120] feet; g) increasing; h) not shown, but check solid line, h(t) feet label for vertical axis; t seconds label for horizontal axis; the endpoints (0,3) and (234,120); suggested scaling: 6 feet per vertical mark and 12 seconds per horizontal mark; plot one more point besides the endpoints.

7. $S = 30.5\ feet; \quad M = 32.75\ feet; \quad L = 36.75\ feet$

8. $side\ length = s = 50\ cm; \quad altitude/height = h = 43.3\ cm$

9. $L = 22\ min.,\ s = 86\ min.,\ w = 27\ min.$

Unit 3: Exponential Functions

3.1 A New Pattern – Introduction to Exponential Functions

3.1 Launch: Cell Growth

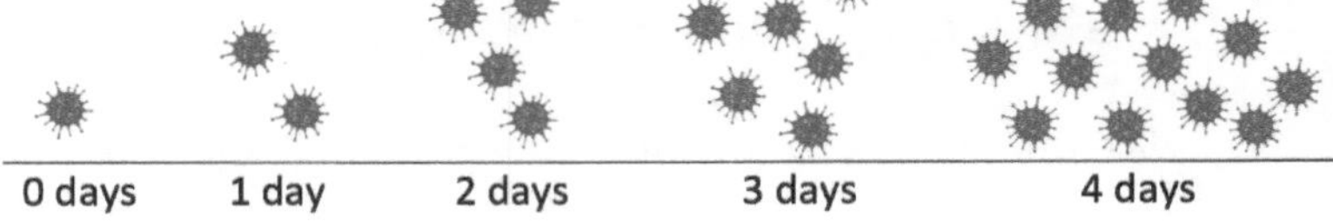

A scientist spent 30 days researching bacteria. After every day, each cell splits into two cells.

cells: WinWin artlab/Shutterstock.com.

a) *Without doing any calculations*, write an estimate for the number of cells after 30 days. Just guess! Be brave!

b) Identify and label the variables including units. Are they discrete or continuous? Explain.

IV (Input): days

DV (Output): number of cells

c) Make a table of values and examine it for a pattern. Is it linear? Justify your answer with calculations. Describe any other patterns you find. multripling by 2

d	N(d)
0	1
1	2
2	4
3	8
4	16
5	

$N(d) = 2^d$

$= 2^0$

$2^1 = 2$

$2^2 = 4$

$2^{30} = 1,073,741,824$

d) After examining the pattern of this function, can you figure out how to write an equation for it?

e) Use the equation to find out how many cells there would be after 30 days. How close was your estimate?

f) Describe the trend of this cell-growth pattern. How does it compare to linear growth?

3.1 Exponential Tables

I. For each table:

- Determine if it is linear, exponential, or neither. Show calculations to justify your answer.
- If the table is linear or exponential, write the function equation.
- Is it increasing or decreasing? Check that your equation matches the trend in the table.

1.

d days	***N*(*d*)** cells
0	24,000
1	30,000
2	37,500
3	46,875

2.

y years	***F*(*y*)** fish
0	1680
1	840
2	420
3	210

3.

m months	***D*(*m*)** dollars
0	250
1	375
2	562.50
3	843.75

4.

t	***P*(*t*)**
0	28,000
1	21,000
2	14,000
3	7,000

5.

d days	$V(d)$ views
2	4500
3	5400
4	6480
5	7776

×1.2
×1.2
×1.2

$V(d) = (1.2)^d$

$4500 = a(1.2)^2$

$\frac{4500}{1.44} = \frac{1.44}{1.44}$

3,125

$V(d) = 3{,}125(1.2)^d$ ✓

6.

h hours	$L(h)$ likes
3	324
4	972
5	2916
6	8748

7.

d days	$N(d)$ cells
5	128,000
6	102,400
7	81,920
8	65,536

8.

x	$F(x)$
9	67,560
10	67,900
11	68,240
12	68,580

II. For each table below.

- Verify that it is exponential and find the constant multiplier. Round the multiplier to ***ten-thousandths***.
- Use substitution to find the initial value rounded to a whole number.
- Write the function equation.

1.

t years since last census	$P(t)$ population of Springfield
3	1,318,200
4	1,713,660
5	2,227,758

2.

m time in minutes	$g(m)$ grams of oxygen-14 remaining
3	34.191
4	18.976
5	10.532

3.

d days	$G(d)$ grams of gold-198 remaining
5	104.88
6	81.07
7	62.67

4.

d days	$I(d)$ grams of iodine-131 remaining
7	65.428
8	59.998
9	55.018
10	50.452

3.1 Exponential Function Equations

I. Write the formula for an exponential function equation. For the constants $\boldsymbol{a}$, and $\boldsymbol{b}$, identify their restrictions, list other names for them, and explain their meaning.

II. For each equation below, determine whether or not it is an exponential function and explain why.
IF it is exponential, determine whether it is *increasing* or *decreasing*, and identify the constants $\boldsymbol{b}$ and $\boldsymbol{a}$.

1. $y = 5(2)^x$

Increasing
value bas greather than 1

2. $y = 200(x)^2$

3. $f(x) = 2.75(16)^x$

4. $g(t) = -55\left(\frac{7}{5}\right)^t$

5. $y = 1300\left(\frac{3}{4}\right)^x$

6. $f(x) = -5x + 4$

7. $y = 16(0.24)^{-x}$ X

No - variable

8. $y = 8(x)^{0.25}$ X

The x should be the exponent

9. $y = 1{,}000{,}000(-10)^x$

10. $y = 10.5(8.6)^x + 4$

11. $N(d) = 20(1)^d$

12. $P(t) = 4500\left(\frac{11}{9}\right)^{-t}$

3.1 Exponential Situations

I. For each exponential situation below, perform the Quantitative Analysis for functions and write the equation..

1. *A 20-year old college student invests $500 in stock. The value of her investment changes by a factor of 1.1 each year until she is 40.*

IV: # of years = t

DV: # of money changing = V(t)

Initial value: 500 constant multiplier: 1.1

Equation: $V(t) = 500(1.1)^t$

Domain: {0, 1, 2, . . ., 20} years since

Range: {500, 550, 605 . . . 3363.75} $

$V(t) = (1.1)^t$

$V(t) = 500(1.1)^t$

2. *A city population is about 3,850,000 in 2030. Suppose that each year after, the population is $\frac{11}{13}$ of what it was the previous year until 2040.*

IV: # of years = t

DV: population = P(t)

Initial value: 3,850,000 constant multiplier: $\frac{11}{13}$

Equation: $P(t) = 3,850,000(0.85)^t$

Domain: [0, 10] # of years

Range: [724359.33, 3,850,000] population

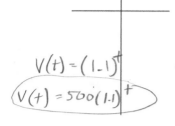

yrs since 2030 t	pop P(t)

3. *A local podcaster starts with 4 listeners. His audience triples every month for his first year.*

IV:

DV:

Initial value: constant multiplier:

Equation:

Domain:

Range:

II. For each exponential situation below,

a) Identify and label the independent/dependent variables including units.
b) Find the constants: multiplier/factor/ratio & initial value.
c) Write an equation for the exponential function. Check that your equation matches the trend of the function.

1. *A 20-pound ice block melts exponentially, and after 1 hour it weighs 15 pounds.*

2. *The median house value in Springfield grew exponentially during a real estate bubble. After the first year it was $200,000 and increased to $230,000 the next year.*

3. *Jerome opened a savings account. After 1 year he had $1030 and after 2 years he had $1060.90.*

4. *A study revealed that a jellyfish population has been changing exponentially. Five years after the study began researchers estimated 2870 jellyfish and six years after it began they estimated 7748 jellyfish in the area.*

3.1 More Tables and Situations

I. For each table: Verify that it is linear, exponential, or neither. Show calculations to support your answer.
IF it is linear or exponential,

- Find the constant rate of change or constant multiplier and the initial value. Round multipliers to hundredths..
- Write the function equation.

1.

t years since 2020	$P(t)$ people
0	6420
1	6370
2	6320
3	6270

2.

s side length	$A(s)$ area (sq. feet)
0	0
1	2.6
2	10.4
3	23.4
4	41.6

3.

t years	$A(t)$ grams left
4	1.6
5	0.32
6	0.064
7	0.0128

4.

x	$f(x)$
35	93.2
36	139.8
37	209.7
38	314.5

5.

w	$C(w)$
40	774.6
41	792.0
42	809.4
43	826.8
44	844.2

6.

x	$P(x)$
18	28147.5
19	22518.0
20	18014.4
21	14411.5

7.

x	$g(x)$
0	1458
2	648
4	288
6	128

8.

x	$f(x)$
4	112
6	448
8	1792
10	7168

9.

x	$D(x)$
4	0.5184
7	0.8958
10	1.5479
13	2.6748

II. For each situation:

- Identify and label the independent and dependent variables.
- Determine and explain why the relationship between the variables is linear **or** exponential.
- Identify the appropriate constants - initial value and either constant rate of change or constant multiplier.
- Write the function equation. Check that your equation matches the trend of the function.
- [Section 3.2] Sketch a graph of the function.

1. An investment of $2,000 in 1970 triples every decade until 2020.

2. An investment of $5000 in 1980 earns $1000 every year until 2020.

3. A population grows by a factor of 1.04 every year from its population of 6000 in 1990.

4. In 1990 the population of a town was 12,000, and every year since then the population is $\frac{15}{14}$ times what it was the previous year.

5. In January a website has 3,000,000 hits. Each month after that it has 20,000 fewer hits than the previous month.

6. In January a website has 9,000,000 hits. Each month after that the number of hits is one third of what it was the previous month.

3.2 Analyzing Exponential Functions

3.2 Launch: Graphing an Exponential

Recall the Cell-Growth problem from section 3.1. *A scientist spent 30 days researching new bacteria. After every day, each cell splits into two cells.* cells: WinWin artlab/Shutterstock.com.

IV: d = the time elapsed since cells began splitting (day)
DV: $C(d)$ = the number of cells in the dish after d days (cell)

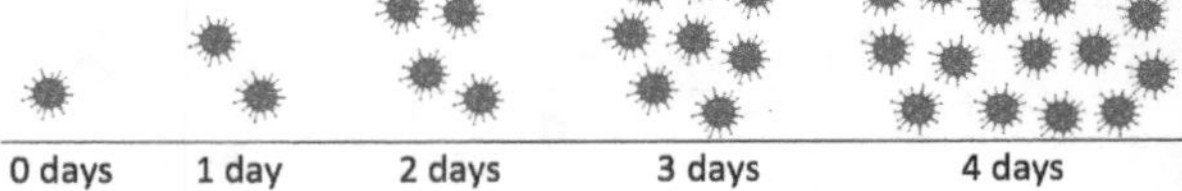

$$C(d) = 1(2)^d$$

a) Fill in the table for days 0 – 5 and 30 to refresh our memory.

d	$C(d)$
0	
1	
2	
3	
4	
5	
30	

b) Write the domain and range for this cell-growth model.

Domain =

Range =

c) Plot a graph on the grid for only the first five days of the model. Why do you think we chose not to graph all 30 days (for now)?

After plotting points for days 0 – 5, add the *hypothetical* negative values $d = -1, -2, -3, -4$ to the table and plot those on the graph. (Why are they hypothetical?)

d) Summarize the characteristics of the exponential growth graph. What word describes its behavior to the left?

1. *A strain of bacteria starts with 200,000,000 cells and every day 1/2 of the cells die.* Let

IV: d = the time elapsed since cells began splitting (day)
DV: $N(d)$ = the number of cells *left alive* in the dish after d days (cell)

d	$N(d)$
0	
1	
2	
3	
4	
5	
	1

a) Fill in the table for days 0 – 5.

b) Check the table for an exponential pattern and write the function equation.

c) To write the domain for this cell-decay model, we need to know when the function no longer models the situation. We must figure out on which day the last cell starts to die. For now we can do this with trial-and-error.

Domain =

Range =

d) Plot a graph on the grid for the first five days of the model.

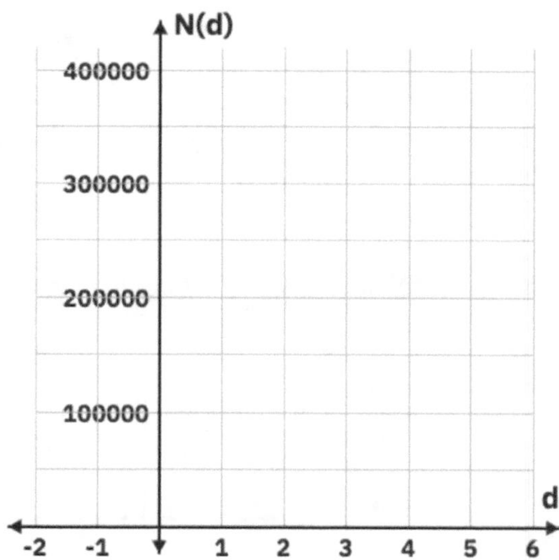

After plotting points for days 0 – 5, add the *hypothetical* negative values $d = -1, -2$ to the table and plot those on the graph. (Why are they hypothetical?)

e) Summarize the characteristics of the exponential decay graph. What word describes its behavior to the right? How does it compare with the exponential growth graph?

3.2 Exponential Graphs

I. Go back to Exponential Situations (1) – (7) in section 3.1 and sketch graphs for those function equations.

II. *Sketch* a graph for each of the following functions on their given domain. Label the vertical intercept.

a) $A(t) = 600\left(\frac{11}{13}\right)^t$ on domain $\{-3, -2, -1, 0, 1, 2, \ldots, 6\}$

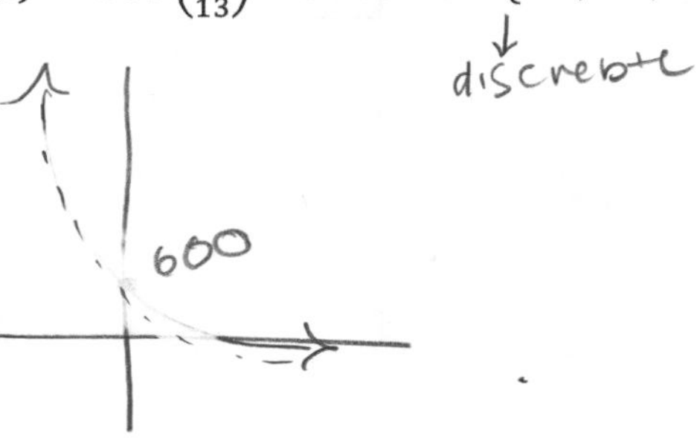

b) $P(n) = 500(2.4)^n$ on domain $[-5, 10]$

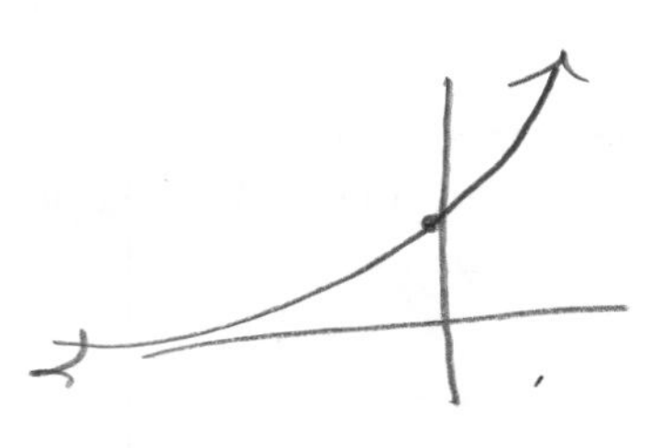

c) $H(w) = \frac{1}{2}\left(\frac{5}{4}\right)^w$ on domain $[-3, 20]$

d) $L(t) = 200(0.6)^t$ on domain $\{-4, -3 \ldots, 10\}$

III. For each graph, write a linear **or** an exponential equation with *numerical* coefficients that could represent it.

A.

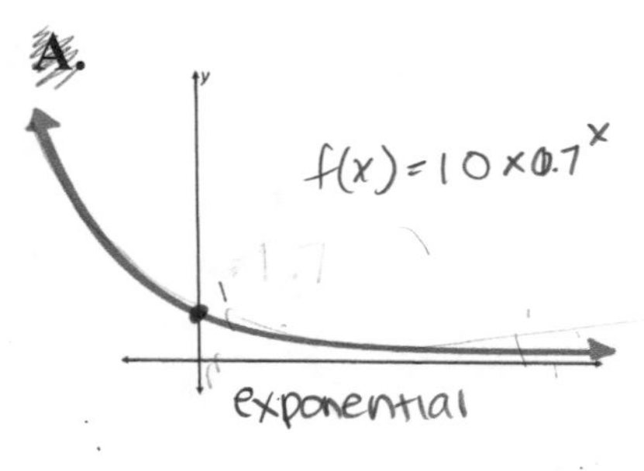

B.

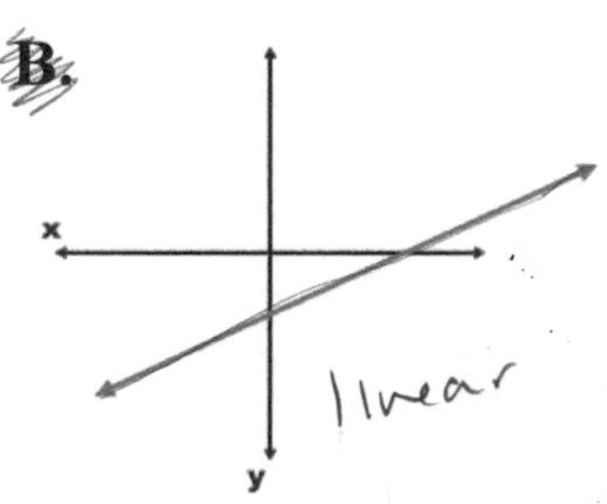

C.

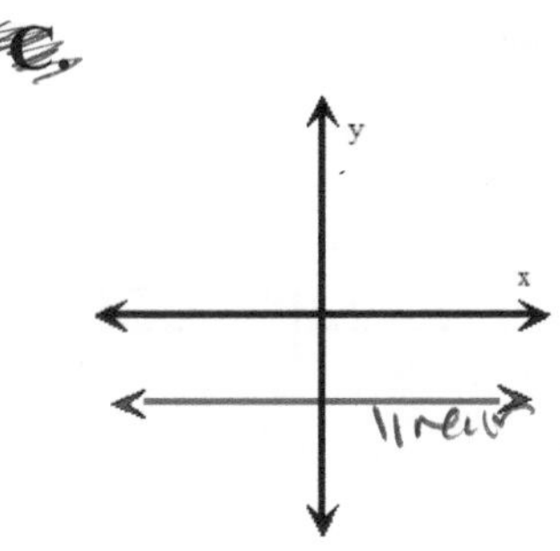

D.

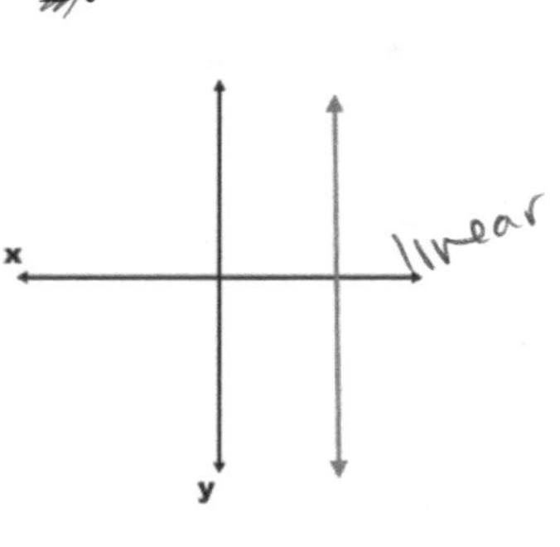

E.

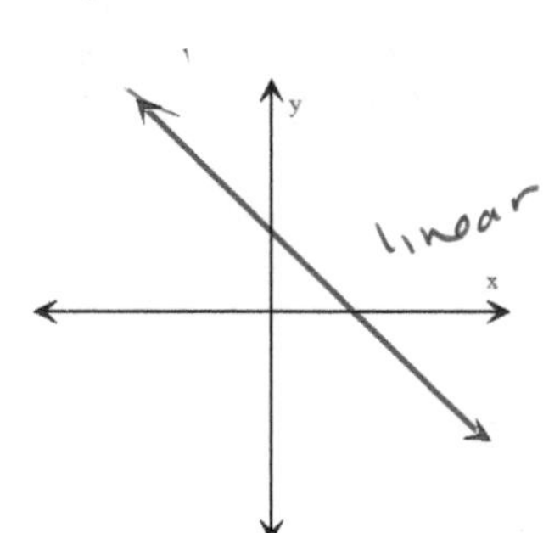

F.

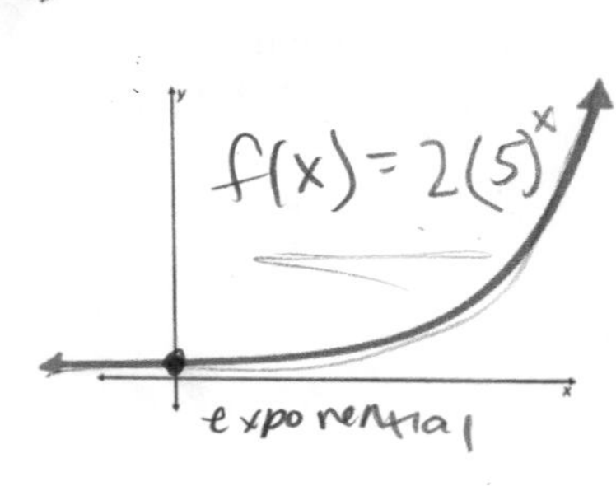

3.2 Solving Exponential Equations with Logarithms

1. Recall our earlier example: *A strain of bacteria starts with 200,000,000 cells and every day 1/2 of the cells die.*

IV: d = the time elapsed since cells began splitting (day)
DV: $N(d)$ = the number of cells *left alive* in the dish after d days (cell)

$$N(d) = 200{,}000{,}000(0.5)^d$$

d	$N(d)$
0	200,000,000
1	100,000,000
	1

To find the endpoint of the domain, we had to find the number of days until the last cell began to die. With trial and error we found that $d \approx 28$ days. The guess-and-check method is far too inefficient and not always precise, so from now on we will use an algebraic approach – solving an exponential equation.
Substituting $N(d) = 1$ we get:

$$1 = 200{,}000{,}000(0.5)^d$$

2. Explain how to recognize an exponential equation.

4. Explain how to solve an exponential equation.

5. Identify each equation as **linear**, **power**, or **exponential**, and then solve it using the appropriate strategy.

a) $3000 = 5(1.05)^t$

$600 = (1.05)^t$

$\frac{\log 600}{\log 1.05}$

131.1

when you have to ~~sto~~ a solve for exponent.

b) $840 = 3(12 - 4b) + 3$

c) $-1800 = 5t^3 + 20$

d) $7p^2 = 231$

e) $40 = 20\left(\frac{2}{3}\right)^t$

f) $994(2.4)^d = 1{,}000{,}000$

3.2 Analyzing Exponential Functions

For each function, analyze the constants in the equation and the trend. Then:

a) Determine the real-world domain and range. Show work to find endpoints.

b) Sketch a graph. LABEL the axes, 'y'-intercept, the endpoints, and the asymptote.

1. *The function* $\mathbf{R(m)} = \mathbf{32(1.5)^{m}}$ *models a rabbit population over a six-month period where* $R(m)$ *is the number of rabbits after* m *months.*

Growth or Decay?

Constant multiplier:

Initial value:

Domain =

Range =

2. *The value of a car is given by the formula* $\mathbf{V(t)} = \mathbf{16,000(0.88)^{t}}$ *in dollars where* t *is the time in years since its purchase.* The model is valid until the car is worth ≈ \$2350.

Growth or Decay?

Constant multiplier:

Initial value:

Domain =

Range =

3. *The amount in grams of a sample of a radioactive substance after* t *decades is given by the function* $A(t) = \mathbf{10,000}\left(\frac{5}{4}\right)^{-t}$ *, and the 'safe' limit is 5 grams.*

Growth or Decay?

Constant multiplier:

Initial value:

Domain =

Range =

3.2 Writing Equations from Exponential Graphs

For each exponential graph:

a) Find the constant ratio/multiplier and the initial value. Show algebraic work.

b) Write an equation for the exponential function.

$W(x) = ab^x$

$W(x) = 10(1.4)^x$

A.

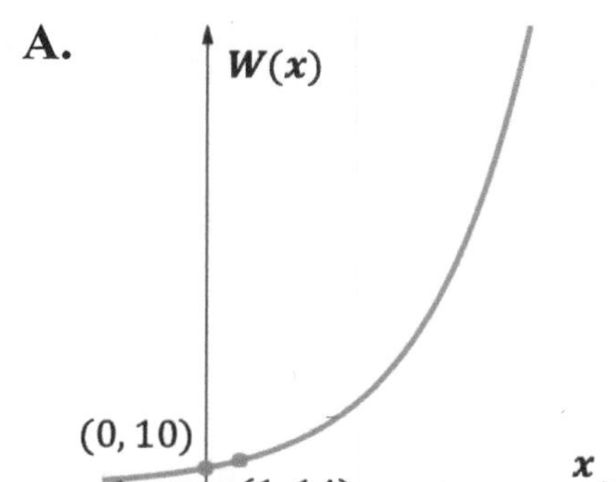

B.

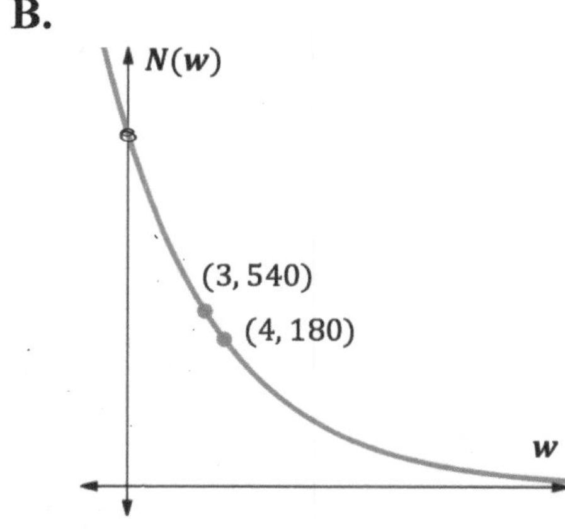

$n(w) = a(0.33)^w$

$540 = a(0.33)^3$

127

$a \approx 14594$

C.

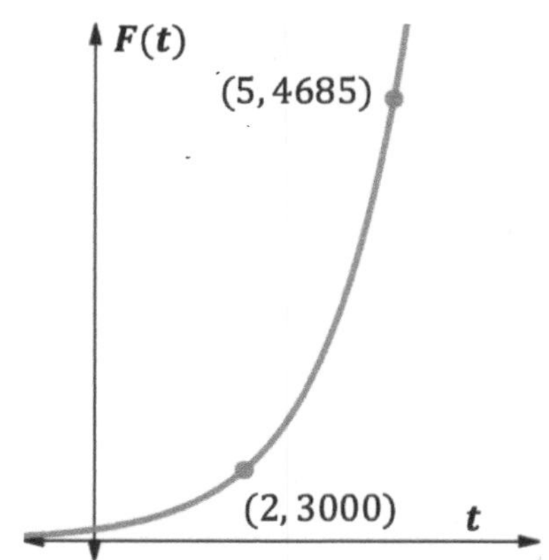

3.2 Comparing Linear and Exponential

I. Determine whether each graph is linear or exponential and write an equation for it using the labeled points. Show algebraic work.

A.

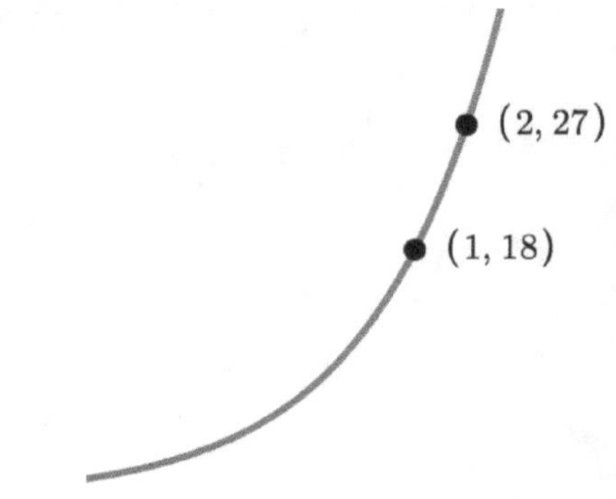

B.

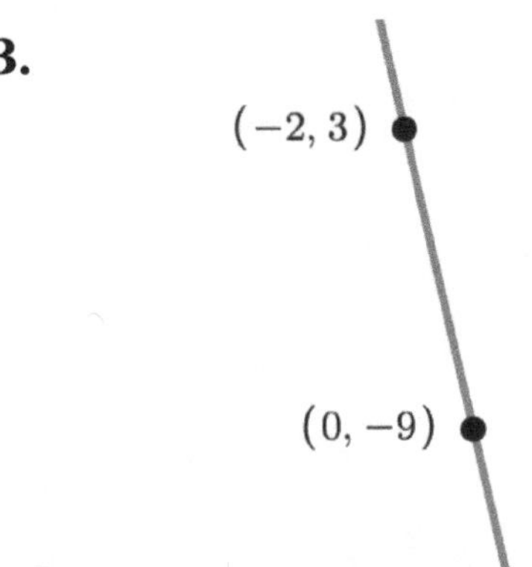

C.

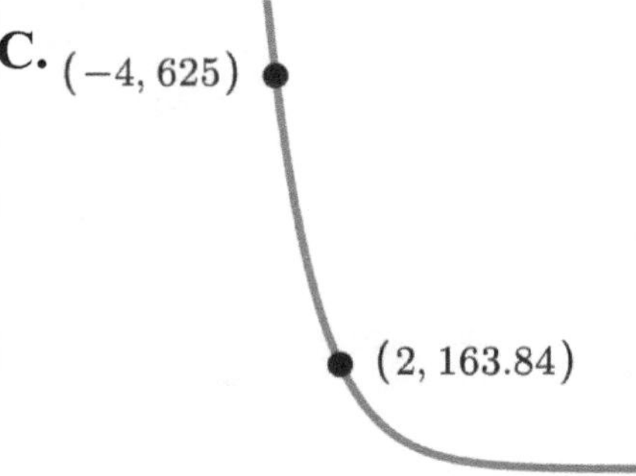

D.

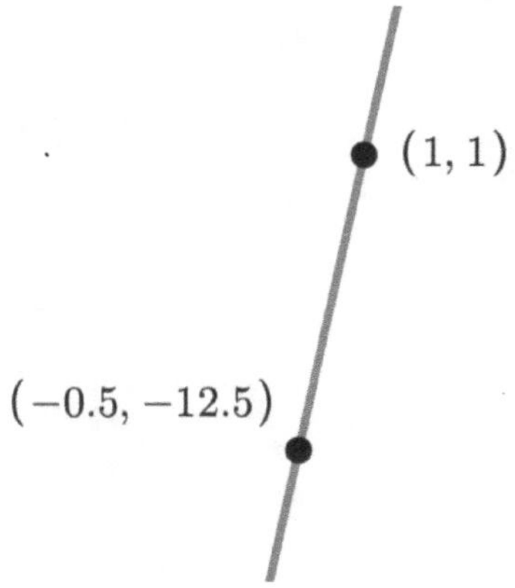

$(1, 1)$

$(-0.5, -12.5)$

II. Write an example of an equation for a function, if any, which satisfies each of the following: If you cannot write such an example, explain why not.

1. An exponential decay function with an initial value of 340.

$f(x) = 340(0.5)^x$

2. An exponential growth function with an initial value of 600.

3. An exponential growth function with an initial value of 0.43.

4. An increasing linear (growth) function with an initial value of 45.

5. A decreasing linear (decay) function with an initial value of 1/2.

6. An exponential function with a base of 5/4. Is it growth or decay?

$f(x) = 5(5/4)^x$ growth

7. An exponential function with a constant multiplier of 1/3. Is it growth or decay?

8. An exponential function with a factor of 4.1. Is it growth or decay?

9. An exponential function with a factor of 0.65. Is it growth or decay?

10. An exponential function with a base of −0.98. Is it growth or decay?

11. A constant function. Is it growth or decay?

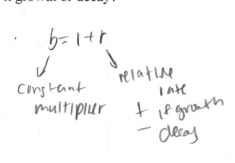

$b = 1 + r$

constant multiplier

relative rate + if growth − decay

3.3 Problem Solving with Exponentials

3.3 Launch: A Growing Colony

A colony of 1024 cells increases every week by $\frac{1}{4}$.

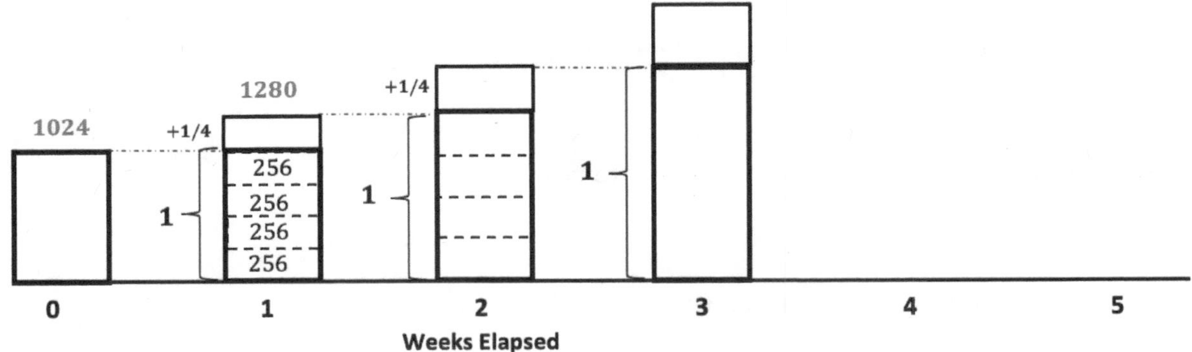

Before we can model this situation, we need to understand what it means to '*increase by* $\frac{1}{4}$' every week. In the diagram above, the height of each bar represents the number of cells in that week.

b) Examine the first two columns in the diagram and explain what the 256 represents.

c) Explain what the 1280 in the second column represents and how it was calculated.

d) Fill in each section of the third column (week 2). How many total cells are there in week 2?

e) Complete the diagram to show the calculation of the number of cells for the first 5 weeks.

f) How does the height of each column compare with the previous one? Are the differences the same? Are the ratios the same? Use information from the completed diagram. You should not do any additional calculations.

g) Do you think that the cells are increasing linearly or exponentially? Explain your reasoning.

h) Identify and label the variables including units.

IV:

DV:

i) Fill in the table and check for both linear and exponential patterns. Show calculations.
If it is exponential, what is the multiplier? Can you find it without using the table?

g) Write the function equation.

Summarizing the Main Concepts

Explain the meaning of a relative rate of change.

How can exponential functions be characterized in terms of their relative rate of change?

What is the relationship between the relative rate of change and the constant multiplier?

3.3 Exponential Situations with Relative Rates

1. *Let's buy a house for $100,000.*

a) Do real estate values increase or decrease? Explain.

Suppose that in our town the value of houses increase by 2% every year.

b) Is this situation linear, exponential, or neither? Explain how you know.

Constants:

IV =

DV =

c) Write the function equation.

2. *A city population of squirrels was 1200 in the year 2000 and increased by* $\frac{3}{42}$ *every year until 2020.*

Constants:

$b = 1 + \frac{3}{42}$

IV =

$b = \frac{15}{14}$ $\left(\frac{45}{42}\right)$

DV =

or 1.07

Equation:

Domain:

Range:

3. *A stamp is purchased for $12 increases in value by 120% every year until it is worth $3000.*

Constants:

IV =

DV =

Equation:

Domain:

Range:

4. *A colony of 3125 cells decreases every week by* $\frac{1}{5}$.

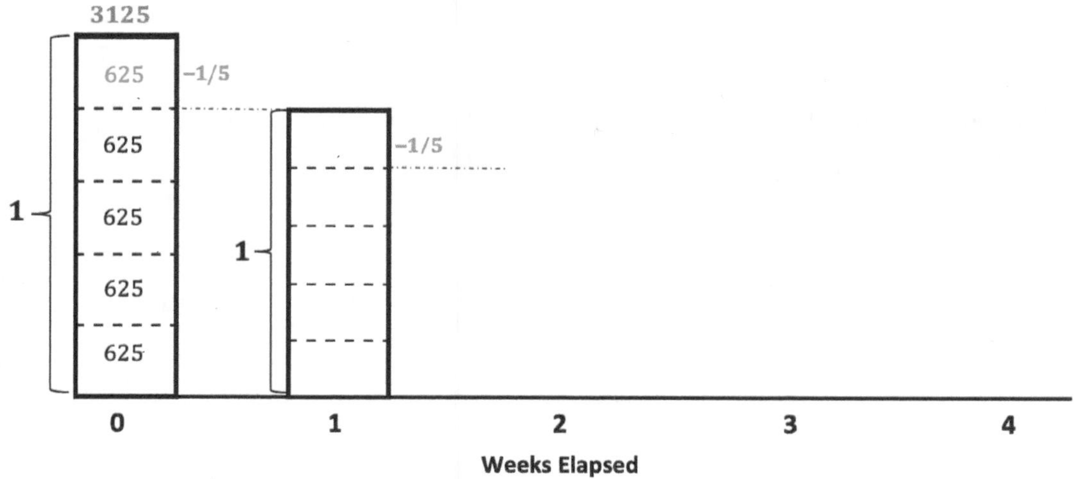

Let's analyze what it means to '*decrease by* $\frac{1}{5}$' every week. The height of each bar in the diagram above represents the number of cells in that week.

a) Examine the first two columns in the diagram and explain what the 625 represents.

b) Calculate the total cells in week 2 and explain how to calculate it.

c) Fill in each section of the second column (week 1) and use it to find the number of cells in week 2.

d) Complete the diagram to show the calculation of the number of cells for the first 4 weeks.

e) How does the height of each column compare with the previous one? Are the differences the same? Are the ratios the same? Use information from the completed diagram. You should not do any additional calculations.

f) Do you think that the cells are decreasing linearly or exponentially? Explain your reasoning.

g) Identify and label the variables including units.

IV:

DV:

h) Fill in the table and check for both linear and exponential patterns. Show calculations.
If it is exponential, what is the multiplier? Can you find it without using the table?

i) Write the function equation.

Summarizing the Main Concepts

Explain the meaning of a relative rate of change.

How can exponential functions be characterized in terms of their relative rate of change?

What is the relationship between the relative rate of change and the constant multiplier?

5. *An investment of $4,000 loses 5.4% every month until it's worth half of its original value.*

Constants:

IV =

DV =

Equation:

Domain:

Range:

6. *A local population of rats was 4700 in the year 2010 and decreased by* $\frac{2}{33}$ *every year until 2020.*

Constants:

IV =

DV =

Equation:

Domain:

Range:

7. An investment of $9,000 increases by 4.3% every year until it's worth $20,000.

Constants:

IV =

DV =

Equation:

Domain:

Range:

8. *An antique toy is purchased for $120 but then decreases in value by 1.6% every month until it's worth $75.*

Constants:

IV =

DV =

Equation:

Domain:

Range:

3.3 Relative Rates in Equations

I. Determine whether or not each equation is exponential. Explain why or why not.
IF it is exponential, identify the **initial value**, the **direction** as growth or decay, the **factor**, and the **relative rate**.

1. $y = 64(1.24)^x$

2. $A(t) = 28{,}000\left(\frac{1}{4}\right)^t$

3. $f(x) = 21(-1.03)^x$

b=1+r
1.24=1+r
-1 -1
.24=r

4. $P(t) = 140{,}000(0.97)^t$

5. $V(t) = 9500\left(\frac{3}{5}\right)^{-t}$

6. $N(w) = 200\left(\frac{57}{49}\right)^w$

3.3 Exponential Modeling

I. For each table, show calculations to determine whether or not it is exponential. IF it is exponential,

a) Identify the **initial value**, the growth/decay **factor**, and the relative growth/decay **rate**.
b) Write an equation for the function.
c) Use the equation to fill in the missing values in the table.

1.

d days	***N*(*d*)** cells
0	24,000
1	30,000
2	37,500
3	46,875
10	
	682,121

2.

d days	$N(d)$ cells
4	20,736
5	15,552
6	11,664
7	8,748
9	
	657

3.

t years since census	$P(t)$ Population
2	2,250,000
3	2,700,000
4	3,240,000
6	
	5,598,720

4.

m months	$V(m)$ dollars
4	40,500.00
6	22,781.25
8	12,814.45
10	7,208.13
	962.17

II. 1. *The value of a house* t *years after its purchase is given by* $\boldsymbol{V(t) = 100,000(1.02)^t}$ *dollars. Assume this model is valid for 40 years.*

Domain:

Range:

a) How much is the house worth after 9 months?

b) How much is the house worth after 4 years?

c) How long will it take for the value of the house to double?

d) You plan to sell the house when it reaches \$250,000 in value. According to this model, how many years will it take for the house to reach that value?

1. *The value of a car* t *years after its purchase is given by* $\boldsymbol{V(t) = 24,500(0.922)^t}$*dollars. Assume this model is valid for 10 years.*

Domain:

Range:

a) What is the car worth 39 months after purchase?

b) How much time will it take for the car to be worth half of its original value?

c) When will the car be worth only \$600?

3. *A doctor administers 500 mg of medicine to a patient. The level of the drug in the bloodstream decreases by* $\frac{1}{15}$ *every hour.*

Constants:

IV =

DV =

Equation:

a) How much medicine is in the bloodstream after 4 hours?

b) If the patient needs at least 150 mg in her blood, after how many hours should she get another dose?

4. *In the 1800s, a Australian farmer, homesick for England, imported 24 wild English rabbits and set them free on his land. For the next six years the rabbit population grew by about 21% each month.*

Constants:

IV =

DV =

Equation:

Domain: Range:

a) How many rabbits were there after 5 months?

b) How many rabbits were there after one year? Two years?

c) Did the population reach a quarter of a million rabbits? If so, after how long in months? In years?

d) Do you think the model remained valid past the 6 years? Explain. (And you can look it up!)

$P(t) = 100(1.1)^t$

relative rate

3.3 Linear versus Exponential

I. Describe in which ways linear and exponential functions are similar, and how they are different.

II. *(Suppose) Humans have finally discovered extraterrestrial life! Scientists study how the alien micro-organisms react to different media. To do that, they place a sample of 10 square inches in each of six sample environments. Here is a summary of their observations.*

Sample #	Observation	Model Equation
1	grows by 4/3 of a square inch every day	
2	grows by a factor of 4/3 every day	
3	grows by 4/3 every day	
4	decays by 3/4 every day	
5	decays by a factor of 3/4 every day	
6	decays by 3/4 of a square inch every day	

Identify and label the variables which are the same for each sample.

IV:

DV:

a) Use the variables above to create a model for each sample that describes its reaction and write it in the table.

b) If the organism is beneficial, which medium should we use?

c) If we want to eliminate the organism completely, which medium should we use?

3.3 Mixed Tables, Situations, and Equations

I. For each table, verify whether it is linear, exponential, or neither. Show calculations to justify your answer. If it is linear or exponential,

- Find the initial value and find the constant rate of change or the multiplier and relative rate. Show work.
- Write the function equation.
- Use the equation to fill in blank spaces in the table.
- Sketch a graph of the function.

1.

d days	*N*(*d*) cells
0	45,000
1	30,000
2	20,000
3	13,333
8	
	780.37

2.

x	*f(x)*
3	1
6	8
9	64
12	512
	5,000

3.

s side length (ft.)	*P(s)* Perimeter of a regular polygon (ft.)
0	0
5	25
10	50
15	75
	206

4.

n	*M(n)*
11	1.500
12	0.750
13	0.375
7	
	12,288
	0

5.

m	*G(m)*
0	–80
2	–72
4	–64
132	448
200	
	0

6.

t	*P(t)*
1	231,000
2	242,550
3	254,677.5
5	
	309,562

II. For each situation:

- Identify and label the independent and dependent variables.
- Write the domain and range.
- Verify whether the relationship between the variables is linear or exponential.
- Identify the initial value and find the constant rate of change or the multiplier and relative rate.
- Write the function equation.
- Sketch a graph of the function.

1. An investment of $1700 decreases by 1.9% every year for 12 years.

2. A new business opens with a debt of $1200 and then loses $400 every month until it's value is –9200 dollars.

3. A wild fire had burned 40 acres when it is first reported and spreads by a factor of 1.2 every day for 2 weeks.

4. A population increases by 75 animals every year from 4800 animals in 2010, and that model is still valid today.

5. An investment of $3000 in 1970 doubles in value every decade until 2020..

6. A student's account increased by 2.8% each year since she deposited $800 until it was worth $1500.

7. In January a website has 900,000 hits. Each month after that it has $\frac{29}{30}$ of the hits it had the previous month.

8. A population of 100 mice at the start of 2015 increased by 105% every month until it was one million.

III. Identify each equation as linear, power, or exponential, and then solve it using the appropriate strategy. Do not round as you solve. Round final answers to hundredths if rounding is necessary.

a) $x^2 + 25 = 0$

b) $400{,}000 = 200{,}000\left(\frac{5}{3}\right)^x$

c) $5(12 - 4n) + 4(22 - 5n) = 200$

d) $10{,}000 = 28{,}000\left(\frac{1}{4}\right)^t$

e) $994(2.4)^d = 1{,}000{,}000$

f) $-50 = 100\left(\frac{2}{3}\right)^t$

g) $1.5(2.6)^h = 600{,}000$

h) $14x^2 - 990 = 4$

i) $19{,}000 = 9{,}500\left(\frac{7}{4}\right)^{-t}$

j) $3072 = (4h)(h)(8h)$

k) $70{,}000 = 140{,}000(0.97)^t$

l) $48{,}000 = (10w)(2w)$

Self-Assessment Test 3: Exponential and Linear Functions

Instructions: For full credit, you must show how you did all of your calculations.
If a problem involves an equation for a function, show work using the equation.
Do NOT round in your calculations. Round final answers to the nearest hundredth if rounding is necessary.

1. For each linear or exponential graph, write an equation with *numerical* coefficients that could represent it.

A.

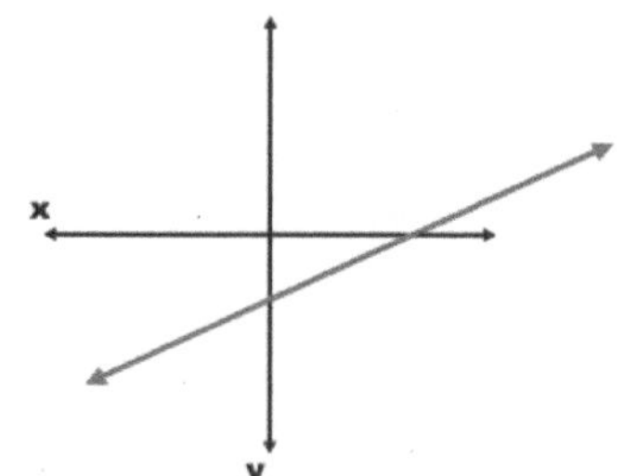

B.

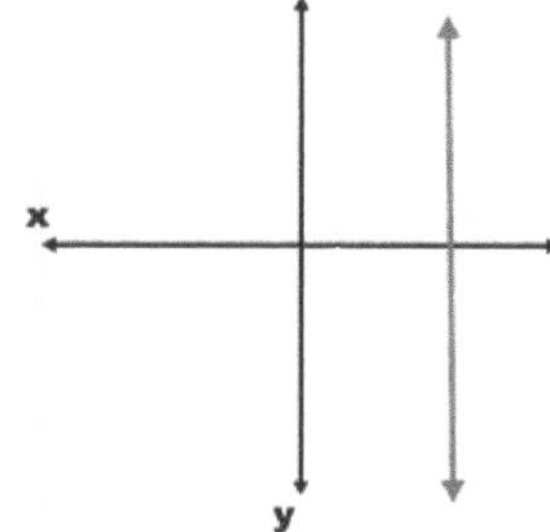

C.

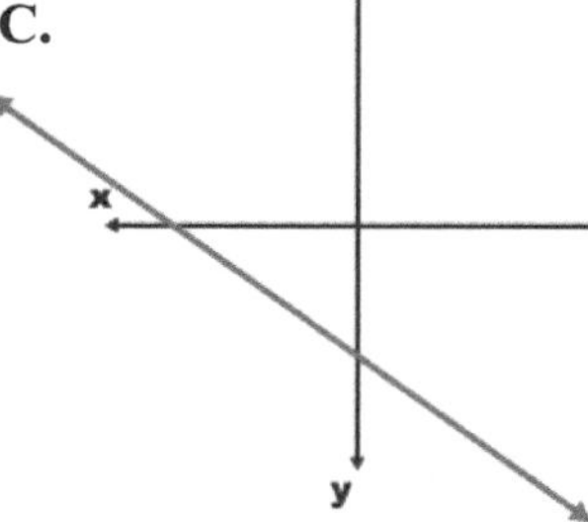

E.

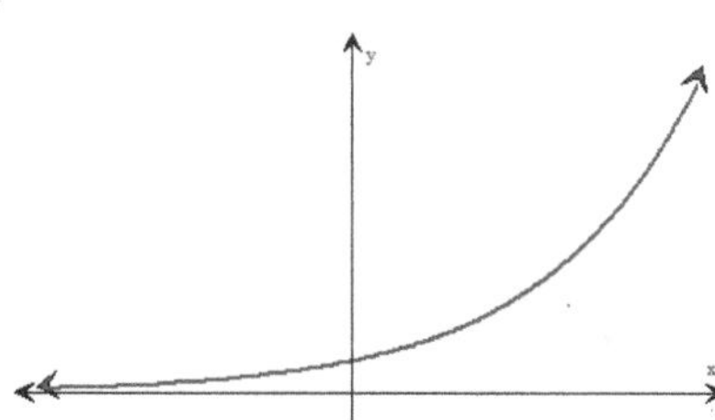

F.

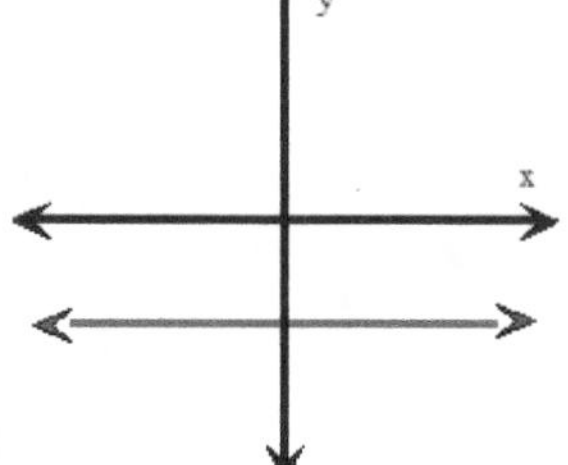

G.

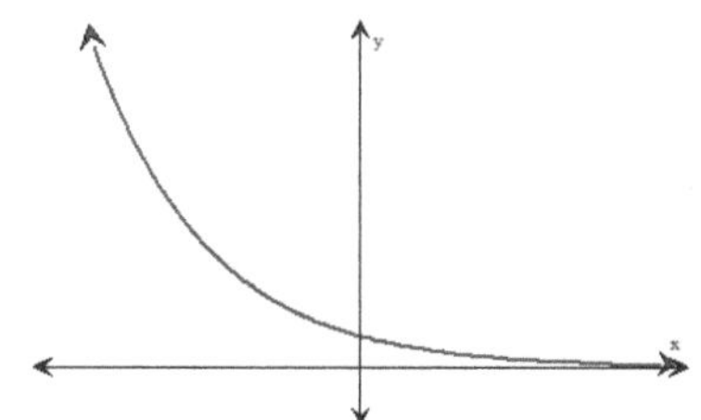

2. *Martin just bought a used car. The dealer told him that the function that models the value of the car in dollars* $\mathbf{t}$ *years after its purchase is:* $\boldsymbol{V(t) = 22,500(0.93)^t}$

a) What did Martin pay for the car?

b) How much can he reasonably sell his car for after 18 months? Round to the nearest dollar.

c) What is the *relative* rate of depreciation for this car? Express the rate as a percentage.

d) How long will it take for the car to be worth $5,000? *Show how to solve algebraically.*
Round to the nearest tenth of a year.

3. How many x-intercepts can a linear function have? Explain and draw sketches of graphs to illustrate.

4. How many x-intercepts can an exponential function have? Explain and draw sketches of graphs to illustrate.

5. *Kaitlyn invested some money into an account to earn annual interest and grow exponentially. After 8 years the amount grew to $1,760.21 and after 9 years to $1,781.33.*

Write an equation for $A(t)$, the amount of money in dollars t years after Kaitlyn invested. Show all calculations.

6. *A colony of 6,000 bacteria decreases at a rate of 1/9 every day.*

a) Identify the independent and dependent variables including their units.

b) Write a function equation that models the situation. Do not use decimals – work in fractions.

c) Give an example of an ordered pair solution other than the initial value, to the equation in (b). Explain what it means in this context.

d) How long until there are 1,000 bacteria left?

e) Write the domain and range for the function.

7. *In January of 2015 the Partridge family bought a house for $220,000 in a town where the home values are increasing by 3.4% every year.*

a) Identify the independent and dependent variables including their units.

b) Write a function equation that represents the situation.

c) What will the home be worth in January of 2035? Round to the nearest dollar.

d) If the growth rate remains the same, how many years (to the nearest tenth of a year) will it take for the house to be worth $500,000? *Show how to solve algebraically.*

8. For each table: Determine whether it represents a relationship that is linear, exponential, or neither. Show calculations to justify and explain your answer.

A.

x	y
1	4
2	10
3	18
4	28

B.

x	y
1	5,400
2	7,200
3	9,000
4	10,800

C.

x	y
1	3,600
2	5,400
3	8,100
4	12,150

9. *A jaguar population decreased at a rate of about 2.2% each year between 1985 and 2015. In 1985 there were an estimated 25,000 jaguars.*

a) Identify and label the independent and dependent variables including units. Use function notation.

b) Write an exponential function equation that models the situation.

c) About how many jaguars were there in 1990? In 1995?

Did we lose the same number of jaguars in each of those 5-year time periods? Explain.

d) In what year did the population reach 16,750 jaguars?

e) According to the model, what would the jaguar population be in 2030? Do you think this is an accurate prediction? Explain.

10. *The number of bacteria cells in a petri dish was 800 and then increased at a rate of 1/9 every day.*

a) Identify and label the two related variables in this situation including their units.

b) Is this a linear or exponential function? Write an equation that represents the situation.

11. *A fish tank is full at a level of 4 feet deep and is going to be drained for cleaning until it's empty. The drain removes water that brings down the level 3 inches every hour.*

a) Identify and label the two related variables in this situation including their units.

b) Is this a linear or exponential function? Write an equation that represents the situation.

Answer Key Test 3

1. Answers may vary. A. $y = 0.5x - 1$; B. $x = 2.7$; C. $y = -x - 3.14$; D. $y = 5(3.4)^x$; E. $y = -5$; F. $y = 78(0.45)^x$
2. a) \$22,500; b) \$20,179; c) 7%; d) ≈ 21 years
3. 0 if it is a non-zero constant function, 1, or infinitely many if it is the constant function $y = 0$
4. None, the x-axis is an asymptote – the graph approaches the x-axis without crossing
5. $A(t) = 1{,}600(1.012)^t$
6. a) IV: d - time (days); DV: $C(d)$ - number of cells (cells); b) $C(d) = 6{,}000\left(\frac{8}{9}\right)^d$; c) $C(10) = 1848$ means the colony will have 1848 cells in 10 days; d) $d \approx 15.2$ days e) Solve for when last cell begins to die: $d \approx 73\ days$. Domain ={0, 1, 2, ...73} days, Range = {1, ..., 6000} cells
7. a) IV: t - time of ownership since 2015 (years); DV: $V(t)$ - value of house (\$); b) $V(t) = 220{,}000(1.034)^t$; c) $V(20) \approx \$429{,}371.74$; d) $t \approx 24.6$ years
8. A. Neither; B. Linear; C. Exponential
9. a) IV: t - time since 1985 (years); DV: $J(t)$ - number of jaguars (jaguars); b) $J(t) = 25{,}000(0.978)^t$; c) In 1990: 22,368 jaguars – a decrease by 2,632; In 1995: 20,014 jaguars – a decrease by 2,354; the function is not linear as the number of jaguars lost every 5 years is not constant; d) 2003; e) 9,187 jaguars; the model is based on data between 1985 and 2015 and it may not be accurate for 2030.
10. a) IV: t - time (days); DV: $N(t)$ - number of cells (cells); b) $N(t) = 800\left(\frac{10}{9}\right)^t$
11. a) IV: t - time (hours); DV: $L(t)$ - water level (inches); b) $L(t) = 48 - 3t$

    OR

    IV: t - time (hours); DV: $L(t)$ - water level (feet); b) $L(t) = 4 - \frac{1}{4}t$

Unit 4 Quadratic Functions

4.1 Problem Solving with Quadratic Equations

4.1 Launch: A Room with a Given Area

A rectangular room has an area of 19 square meters, and its width is 3 meters less than its length. What are the dimensions of the room?

a) Perform the quantitative analysis for *problem solving*.

Labeled Diagram:

Constant(s)

value	unit	detailed description of the quantity

Variables

label	unit	detailed description of the quantity

b) Translate the requirements into symbolic language using your labels above. Write any other formula(s) that relate the quantities in this situation.

c) Solve the system of equations algebraically to find the dimensions of the room.

d) What new equation-solving strategy did you use to solve the system?

e) How many solutions did you find in part (c)? Are all the solutions valid? Explain.

f) Check your valid solution(s).

4.1 The Quadratic Formula

I. Summarize the new equation-solving strategy we are using in this section.

Write the **Standard Form of a Quadratic Equation**:

Define the **Quadratic Formula**:

How many real solutions can a quadratic equation have? Explain how the Quadratic Formula tells us the number of real solutions an equation will have.

II. For each equation, determine the number of real solutions without solving the equation. Then solve the equation algebraically, including complex solutions.

1. $x^2 + x = -1$

2. $G^2 - 1 = G$

3. $2n^2 = 12n - 18$

4. $-3t^2 - 7t - 2 = 0$

5. $4t^2 + 24t = -20$

6. $25x + 620 = 5x^2$

7. $(3w - 2)^2 + 5 = 4w^2$

8. $5 + (x - 3)^2 + 2 = 7$

9. $24.6n + n^2 = 2358.72$

10. $2x^2 - 110x + 1000 = -512.5$

11. $d^2 + (2d - 1)^2 = 10$

12. $h^2 + 658 = 101h$

4.1 Quadratic Problems

1. *A rectangular window has a stick for support across its diagonal. The height of the window is 12 inches shorter than the stick, and the width of the window is 2 feet shorter than the stick. What are the dimensions of the window?*

a) Perform the quantitative analysis for *problem solving*.

Constant(s)

Labeled Diagram:

value	unit	detailed description of the quantity

Variables

label	unit	detailed description of the quantity

b) Translate the requirements into symbolic language using your labels above. Write any other formula(s) that relate the quantities in this situation.

c) Solve the system of equations algebraically to find the dimensions of the window.

b) How many solutions did you find in part (c)? Check your solution(s). Are all the solutions valid? Explain.

2. *Find the base of a triangle if the sum of the base and its altitude is 12 cm, and the area of the triangle is*
   a. *18 square centimeters*
   b. *19 square centimeters*

a) Perform the quantitative analysis for *problem solving*. Diagram:

a) Translate the requirements into symbolic language. Write any other related formula(s).

b) Solve the system to find the base of the triangle with an area of 18 square centimeters.

d) Solve the system to find the base of the triangle with an area of 19 square centimeters.

4.1 Special Cases of Quadratic Problems

1. *A cylindrical glass is 6 inches tall and can hold 42.4 cubic inches of water. What is the radius of the glass?*

Glass: White Space Illustrations/Shutterstock.com

a) Perform the quantitative analysis for *problem solving.*

b) Translate the requirements into symbolic language.

Write any other related formula(s).

b) Solve the system to find the radius of the glass.

d) What special case of a quadratic equation results from the system? What are the two ways can use you solve it?

e) Check your solution(s).

2. *A ladder is leaning against a wall such that its top is at the top of the wall. If the ladder is 1 foot longer than the height of the wall and its base is 6 feet away from the wall, how high is the wall?*

a) Perform the quantitative analysis.

c) Translate the requirements into symbolic language.

Write any other related formula(s).

b) Solve the system to find the height of the wall.

d) What special case of 'quadratic' equation results from the system?

e) Check your solution(s).

4.1 More Quadratic Problem Solving

1. *A rectangular mirror has a height that is ½ foot taller than its width and an area of 216 square inches. What are the dimensions of the mirror?*

a) Perform the quantitative analysis.

Diagram:

d) Translate the requirements into symbolic language.

Write any other related formula(s).

b) Solve for the dimensions of the mirror.

2. *A box is 20 centimeters wide, and its length is 17 centimeters more than its depth. If its volume is 29,760 cubic centimeters, what is the length of the box?*

a) Perform the quantitative analysis for *problem solving.*

Diagram:

b) Translate the requirements into symbolic language.

Write any other related formula(s).

c) Solve for the length of the box.

3. *A child's playhouse has the shape of a triangular prism. The front face is a triangle with the base 2 feet more than the height. The prism is 9 feet long from front to back and its volume is 450 cubic feet. What is the height of the playhouse? What is the base of the triangular opening?* Children: Colorfuel Studio/Shutterstock.com

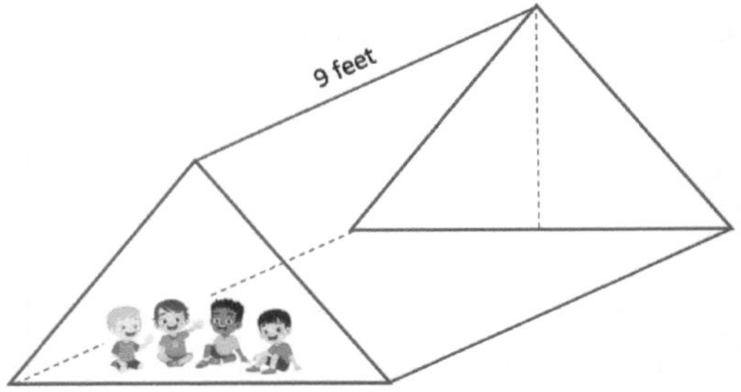

a) Perform the quantitative analysis.

b) Translate the requirements into symbolic language.

Write any other related formula(s).

c) Solve for the tent's height and the base of the opening.

4. *A 10-foot tree is broken by a storm, so the tip of the tree falls to the ground 5 feet away from the base of the tree. How tall is the stump of the tree that is still standing?* Tree: TINA NIZOVA?Shutterstock.com

a) Perform the quantitative analysis.

b) Translate the requirements into symbolic language.

Write any other related formula(s).

c) Solve for the height of the stump.

5. *If the face of a cube has an area of 25 square centimeters, what is the volume of the cube?*

Perform the quantitative analysis.

Diagram:

a) Translate the requirements into symbolic language.

Write any other related formula(s).

b) Solve for the volume of the cube.

4.1 Quadratic Systems of Equations

1. $\begin{cases} x = 12 - y \\ 1486 = -6xy \end{cases}$

2. $\begin{cases} y = x - 3 \\ x = y^2 - 2y + 5 \end{cases}$

3. $\begin{cases} b = h - 2 \\ b = h^2 + 7h + 6 \end{cases}$

4. $\begin{cases} LW = 50.16 \\ W = L - 7 \end{cases}$

5. $\begin{cases} w = 2t + 3 \\ w^2 = t^2 + t - 3 \end{cases}$

6. $\begin{cases} L = 3W + 1 \\ L^2 + W^2 = 1{,}020.2 \end{cases}$

7. $\begin{cases} w = 2t + 3 \\ t^2 + t - 3 = w \end{cases}$

8. $\begin{cases} \frac{1}{2}bh = 4214 \\ h = b + 12 \end{cases}$

4.1 Extra Quadratic Problems

1. *A child's slide can be thought of as the hypotenuse of a right triangle. Compared to the base of the triangle, the length of the slide is 12 inches longer and the height is 11.5 feet shorter. What is the length of the slide?*

2. *A square and a rectangle have the same area. The side of the square is double the width of the rectangle. What is the area of the square if the perimeter of the rectangle is 10 meters?*

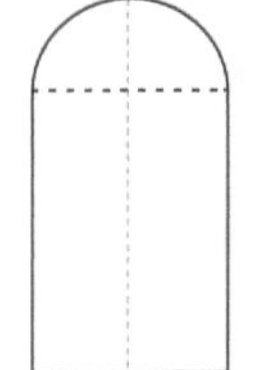

3. *A Norman window is 12 feet tall, and its area is 46.28 square feet. How wide is the window? A Norman window has the shape of a rectangle with a semicircle on top.*

4. *A right triangle has the sum of the legs* $\sqrt{2}$ *centimeters, and the area 0.25 square cm. How long is the hypotenuse?*

5. *The difference between two numbers is 61 and their product is 15,326. What are the two numbers?*

6. *The sum of two numbers is* 18 *and their product is* -943. *What are the two numbers?*

7. *The sum of the squares of two consecutive even integers is 340. What are the numbers?*

8. *A rectangular window has an area of 9,928 square centimeters, and its length is 10 centimeters more than 2 times it width. What are the dimensions of the window?*

9. *The diagonal path across a rectangular field is 538 feet and the width of the field is 382 feet less than the length. What is the perimeter of the field?*

10. *A box in the shape of a rectangular prism has a width of 34 inches and a length that is 2 feet more than its depth. If the volume of the box is 34,408 cubic inches, what are the length and the depth of the box?*

11. *A triangle has a base that is 8.5 centimeters less than its altitude (height). If the area of the triangle is 1356 square centimeters, how long is the base of the triangle? What is its altitude?*

4.2 Another New Pattern – Intro to Quadratic Functions

4.2 Launch: A Square Garden

We are planning a square-shaped garden inside a 40-by-50-foot yard. Let

IV: s = side length of the square garden (foot)
DV: $A(s)$ = area of the square garden (square foot)

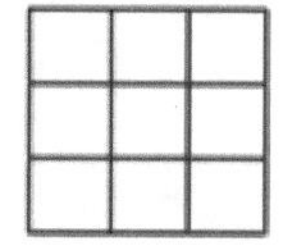
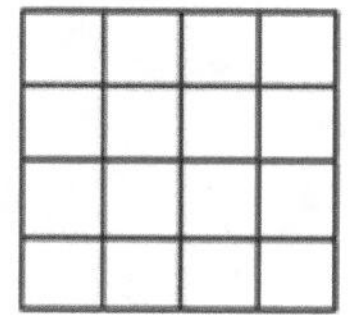
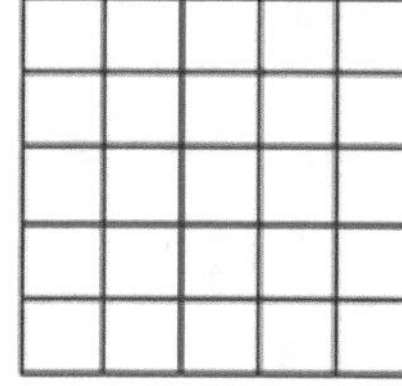

Domain =

Range =

s	$A(s)$
0	
1	
2	
3	
4	
5	

Fill in the table of values for s = 1, 2, 3, 4, 5 feet and the endpoint. Check the table for a pattern. Is it linear? exponential? Describe any patterns you see.

Plot a graph for the first five feet of the model.

After plotting points for inputs 0–5, add the *hypothetical* negative values $s = -1, -2, -3, -4$ to the table and plot those on the graph. (Why are they hypothetical?)

Write an equation (formula) to represent the function.

Describe the characteristics of the table and of the graph of this new function. What is this type of function called?

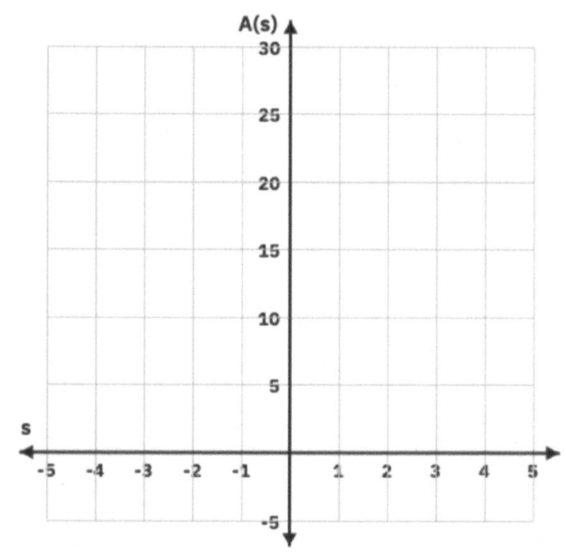

4.2 Quadratic Function Equations

I. Write down the standard form for the function equation for each type of function below. Specify any meanings and constraints on the constants.

Linear:

Exponential:

Quadratic:

II. For each function, determine whether it is quadratic or not and explain why. If it is quadratic, identify the coefficients ***a***, ***b***, and ***c*** of the standard form.

1. $y = 3x - 4x^2 + 7$
2. $s(t) = 20 - 5t + 11t^2$
3. $r(s) = -s^2$
4. $f(x) = 2(.06)x$
5. $h(t) = -16t^2 + 10t + 1$
6. $y = 9m^2 - 40$
7. $r(t) = 11t^3 + 64t - 3$
8. $k(x) = 32x - 4$
9. $A(w) = 86w - 2w^2$

4.2 Quadratic Tables

I. Describe with words, formulas, and examples, the table patterns for linear, exponential, and quadratic functions.

Linear:

Exponential:

Quadratic:

II. Fill in the table of values for each function and calculate the second differences for the output.

1. $f(x) = 5x^2 + 3 - 2x$

x	$f(x)$
1	
3	
5	
7	
9	

2. $g(x) = 7x^3 + 3x^2 - 8$

x	$g(x)$
1	
3	
5	
7	
9	

III. Determine whether each table is linear, exponential, quadratic, or none of those, and justify it with calculations.

1.

d	$N(d)$
0	–8
1	–2
2	16
3	46
4	88

2.

t	$P(t)$
2	–6
4	–30
6	–54
8	–78
10	–102

3.

m	$A(m)$
0	320
1	400
2	500
3	625
4	781.25

4.

x	$F(x)$
9	27
10	35
11	44
12	54
13	65

5.

x	$H(x)$
4	–59
5	–78
6	–99
7	–122
8	–147

6.

p	$N(p)$
2	45
4	145
6	325
8	585
10	925

7.

t	$N(t)$
1	1620
2	2160
3	2880
4	3840

8.

t	$A(t)$
5	25
6	14
7	1
8	–14
9	–31

9.

m	$A(m)$
8	1800
9	1275
10	750
11	225
12	–300

10.

x	$L(x)$
2	4
3	43
4	100
5	175
6	268

11.

d	$H(d)$
13	4
14	1
15	0
16	1
17	4

12.

n	$T(n)$
4	8
5	8
6	8
7	8
8	8

4.2 Quadratic Graphs

I. Draw sketches of graphs for linear and exponential functions on $x - y$ axes. Include increasing, decreasing, and constant examples. Of which type is a constant function? Label asymptotes on graphs that have them.

Linear:

Exponential:

II 1. What is the name for a quadratic graph?

2. Draw a sketch of a quadratic graph. Describe its shape and some of its features. (You'll learn more in 4.3.)

3. Which features make them useful? Give some real-world uses and examples of quadratic-graph shapes.

4.2 Writing Quadratic Function Equations from Tables (Optional)

I. How is the second difference in a quadratic table related to the function equation when the input difference = 1. If the input difference = d? Use your own words to describe how to find the function equation from a quadratic table.

II. Copy the quadratic tables from the section **Quadratic Tables** III into your notebook and find their equations.
III. Write the function equation for each of the quadratic tables below.

1.

x	$F(x)$
4	104
5	163
6	236
7	323
8	424

2.

x	$G(x)$
3	–50
4	–76
5	–110
6	–152
7	–202

3.

x	$H(x)$
8	298
10	430
12	586
14	766
16	970

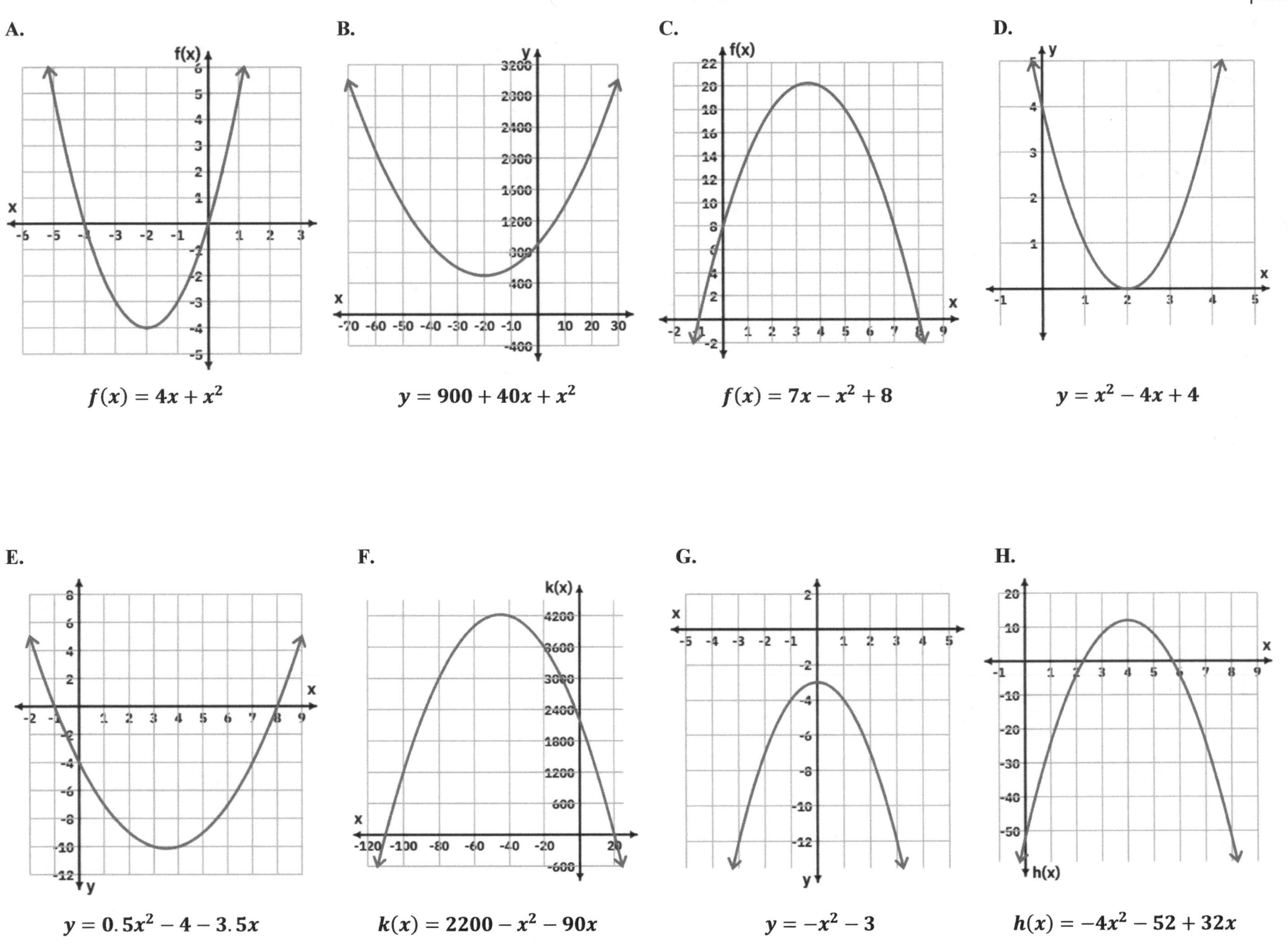

A. $f(x) = 4x + x^2$

B. $y = 900 + 40x + x^2$

C. $f(x) = 7x - x^2 + 8$

D. $y = x^2 - 4x + 4$

E. $y = 0.5x^2 - 4 - 3.5x$

F. $k(x) = 2200 - x^2 - 90x$

G. $y = -x^2 - 3$

H. $h(x) = -4x^2 - 52 + 32x$

4.3 Finding Features of Parabolas Algebraically

4.3 Launch: Analyzing Parabolas

Work in pairs to fill in the table about the graphs on the opposite page. Look for patterns in the table. Then answer the questions below.

	Coefficients			Direction	Vertex (Type)	Axis of Symmetry	*y*-intercept	*x*-intercept(s)
A	a =	b =	c =					
B	a =	b =	c =					
C	a =	b =	c =					
D	a =	b =	c =					
E	a =	b =	c =					
F	a =	b =	c =					
G	a =	b =	c =					
H	a =	b =	c =					

1) What do the equations of the graphs that open up have in common? That open down?

2) What do the graphs with a lowest point have in common? Highest point?

3) Draw the mirror line about which the graph has symmetry. Where does this axis of symmetry intersect the graph?

4) Do *all* the graphs have a *y*-intercept? Explain.

Are there any *x*-intercepts? If yes, how many? Where are they located with respect to the mirror line?

5) Make as many conjectures about the connections between the concepts in the table as you can. Summarize them as a class.

4.3 Graphing Quadratics Using Important Features

I. Find the **direction**, **axis of symmetry** and **vertex**, of each quadratic function (1) – (6). *Show all work.*
II. Algebraically find the **vertical** and the **horizontal intercepts** for each function. Enter all points in a table.
III. Graph each function. Include the axis of symmetry and label axes and important points on your graph.

1. $f(x) = x^2 - 8x + 12$

I. Direction:

Axis of symmetry:

Vertex:

II. Vertical intercept:

Horizontal intercept(s):

III.

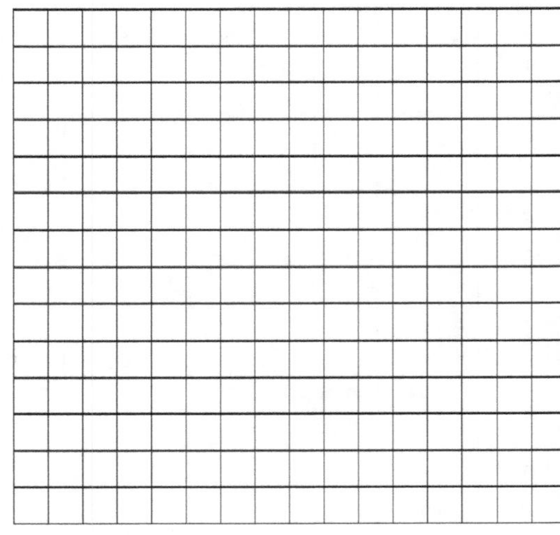

Mirror point of vertical intercept:

2. $y = x^2 - 10x + 25$

I. Direction:

Axis of symmetry:

Vertex:

II. Vertical intercept:

Horizontal intercept(s):

III.

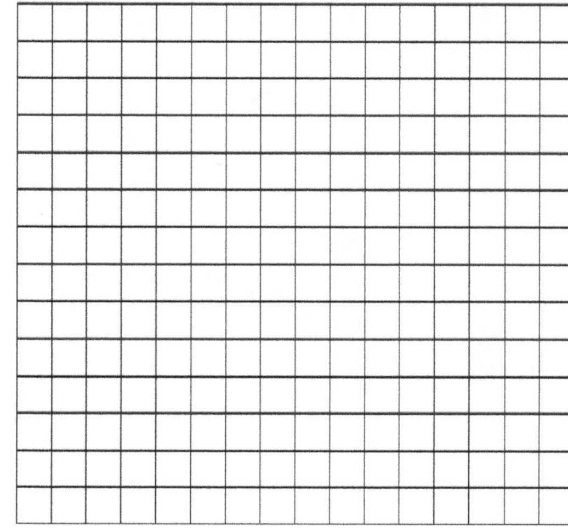

Mirror point of vertical intercept:

3. $P(t) = t^2 + 60t + 1800$

I. Direction:

Axis of symmetry:

Vertex:

II. Vertical intercept:

Horizontal intercept(s):

III.

Mirror point of vertical intercept:

4. $h(x) = -x^2 + 40t + 9600$

I. Direction:

Axis of symmetry:

Vertex:

II. Vertical intercept:

Horizontal intercept(s):

III.

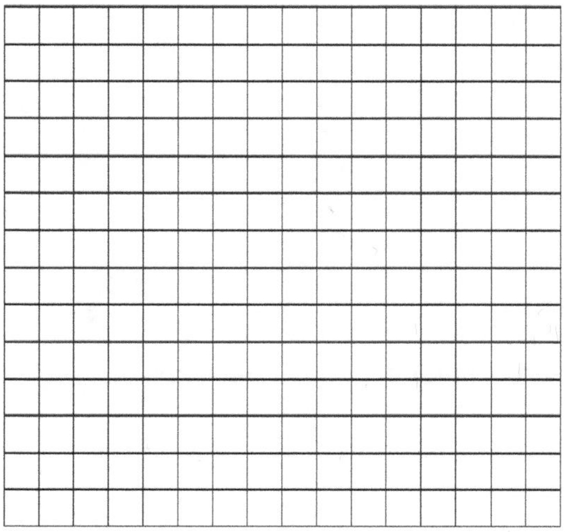

Mirror point of vertical intercept:

5. $M(d) = 2d^2 + 5d - 1$

I. Direction:

Axis of symmetry:

Vertex:

II. Vertical intercept:

Horizontal intercept(s):

III.

Mirror point of vertical intercept:

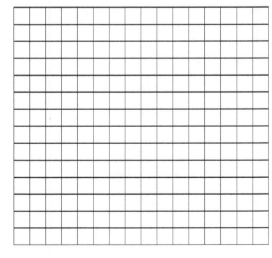

6. $L(n) = 2n^2 - 190n + 3900$

I. Direction:

Axis of symmetry:

Vertex:

II. Vertical intercept:

Horizontal intercept(s):

III.

Mirror point of vertical intercept:

4.3 Summarizing Features of Parabolas

Given a quadratic function $\boldsymbol{f(x) = ax^2 + bx + c}$, its graph is called a **parabola**.

1. What do we mean when we talk about the **direction** of a parabola? Explain how you know from the function equation which direction the parabola will have.

2. Parabolas are **symmetric**. What does that mean? Write the formula for the **axis of symmetry** of a parabola.

3. Every parabola has a **vertex**. Describe the vertex in your own words including the two types.

   Explain how to algebraically find *both* coordinates of the **vertex** from the function equation.

4. Explain how to algebraically find both coordinates of the **$\boldsymbol{y}$-intercept** from the function equation.

5. Explain how to algebraically find both coordinates of the **$\boldsymbol{x}$-intercept(s)** from the function equation.

   How many **$\boldsymbol{x}$-intercept(s)** can a parabola have? Draw sketches to illustrate the possibilities.

4.3 Critical Thinking

1. If a parabola has an x-intercept at $(20, 0)$ and axis of symmetry $x = 9$, find the other -intercept. (Hint: Sketch a graph.)

2. Find the mirror point of (–2, 14) on a parabola with axis of symmetry $x = 6$.

3. Find the mirror point of $(0, -10)$ on a parabola with vertex $(5, -18)$.

4. If a parabola has an x-intercept at $(42, 0)$ and another at $(58, 0)$, what is its axis of symmetry?

5. A parabola has a minimum at $(60, 0)$ and has a y-intercept at $(0, 100)$. What can you say about the x-intercepts of this function. Find another point on its graph.

6. Write an equation for a quadratic function ...

a) that has a minimum an no x-intercepts.

b) that has a maximum and one x-intercept.

c) with two x-intercepts. Does it open up or down? How do you know?

4.3 More Graphing Parabolas

Copy each function equation into your notebook. Find the **direction**, **axis of symmetry**, **vertex**, **y-intercept**, and any **x-intercept(s)** for each function. Then graph the parabola.

1. $P(x) = -20x^2 + 2000x - 32{,}000.$

2. $h(t) = -0.82t^2 + 36t + +3$

3. $f(x) = x^2 + 484 + 44x$

4. $y = 4x^2 + 8x + 30$

4.4 Analyzing Quadratic Functions

4.4 Launch: A Projectile Motion Graph

An astronaut throws a ball to a fellow astronaut on the Moon. The height of the ball, $\mathbf{h}$*, in feet is given by the equation.* $\mathbf{h(t)} = -\mathbf{2.7t^2} + \mathbf{35t} + \mathbf{7}$ *where* $\mathbf{t}$ *is the number of seconds since the ball is thrown.*

Answer the following questions using the graph:

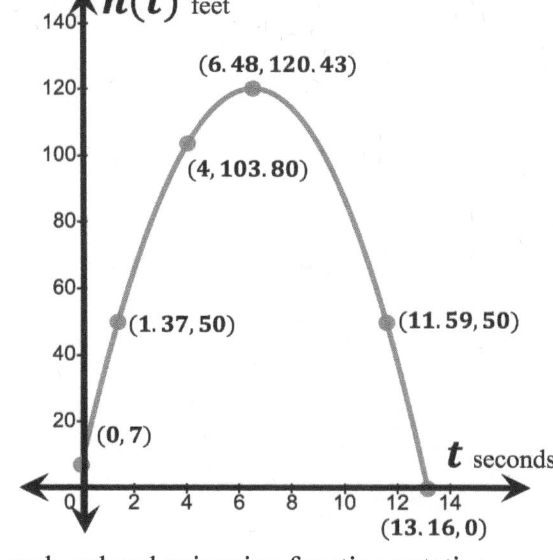

a) Are the variables discrete or continuous? Explain.

b) What are the real-world domain and range of the function?

c) Each ordered pair below is a point on the graph of $\mathbf{h(t)}$. Write each ordered pair using function notation. Then explain its meaning in the context of the situation including units. Identify the intercepts and the vertex.

(0, 7)

(1.37, 50)

(4, 103.80)

(6.48, 120.43)

(11.59, 50)

(13.16, 0)

4.4 Quadratic Modeling

Show how to answer each question *algebraically*. Write answers as ordered pairs *and* in function notation, enter them in a table, and sketch a graph.

1. *An astronaut throws a ball to a fellow astronaut on the moon. The height of the ball,* **h**, *at time* **t** *is given by the equation,* $\mathbf{h(t)} = -2.7t^2 + 35t + 7$, *where* **h** *is in feet and* **t** *is the number of seconds after the ball is thrown.*

a) How high is the ball after 4 seconds?

b) When does the ball reach 200 feet?

c) How high does the ball get?

d) When does it reach that height?

e) When will the ball hit the ground?

Continued: *An astronaut throws a ball to a fellow astronaut on the moon. The height of the ball,* **h**, *at time* **t** *is given by the equation* $\mathbf{h(t)} = -\mathbf{2.7t^2} + \mathbf{35t} + \mathbf{7}$, *where* **h** *is in feet and* **t** *is the number of seconds after the ball is thrown.*

f) When does the ball reach 100 feet?

g) When does the ball reach 5 feet?

h) What was the initial height of the ball when the astronaut released the ball?

i) Give the contextual (real-world) domain and range for this function.

j) Sketch the graph. Label axes, all 'important' points, and all ordered-pair answers to the questions.

Show how to answer each question *algebraically*. Write answers as ordered pairs *and* in function notation, enter them in a table, and sketch a graph.

2. *The weekly profit,* **P** *in dollars, that the Kandy-n-Kakes Company earns depends on* **x** *pounds of designer treats that they make and sell per week. Their kitchen can produce up to 100 pounds of treats per week, and the function is given by the equation* $\mathbf{P(x) = -x^2 + 100x - 1600}$.

a) What will be the profit if K-n-K makes and sells 35 pounds?

b) What will be the profit if K-n-K makes and sells 10 pounds? 100 pounds?

c) How many pounds must K-n-K sell to break-even? Explain.

d) If K-n-K earns a weekly profit of $500, how many pounds did they make and sell?

e) Write the $P(x)$-intercept in function notation and explain its meaning in context including units.

Continued: *The weekly profit,* **P** *in dollars, that the Kandy-n-Kakes Company earns depends on* $\boldsymbol{x}$ *pounds of designer treats that they make and sell. Their kitchen can produce up to 100 pounds of treats per week, and the function is given by the equation* $\boldsymbol{P(x) = -x^2 + 100x - 1600.}$

f) How many pounds must K-n-K make and sell to maximize profit?

g) What is the maximum weekly profit they can earn?

h) Give the contextual (real-world) domain and range for this function.

i) Sketch the graph. Label axes, all 'important' points, and all ordered-pair answers to the questions.

3. *A local theater must decide how much to charge for each ticket to their new play. The theater figures out that their profit in dollars for each show,* $\boldsymbol{P(x)}$*, depends on the ticket price in dollars,* $\boldsymbol{x}$*, and is given by the function:* $\boldsymbol{P(x) = -15x^2 + 1200x - 18,000}$.

a) How much profit does the theater earn if they charge $25?

b) For this function, $P(70) = -7500$. Explain what that means in context.

c) What ticket price(s), to the nearest cent, should the theater charge to break even?

d) What did the theater charge if the profit was $2000?

e) What is the maximum profit the theater can earn for a show?

f) Sketch a graph for this function.

4.4 Creating Quadratic Functions – Optimization Problems

1. *A farmer has 100 meters of fence to enclose a rectangular plot of land having one side along the river. If no fence is needed along the river, find the maximum area that can be enclosed.*

Let $\boldsymbol{x}$ = the length of the side perpendicular to the river (meter)
$\boldsymbol{y}$ = the length of the side parallel to the river (meter)
$\boldsymbol{A}$ = the area of the plot (square meter)

a) The variables have been identified above. Label the diagram with the variables.

b) Identify the constant.

c) Write formulas that relate the variables.

d) Substitute to get a formula for the area, $\boldsymbol{A}$, in terms of one of the other variables. What kind of formula is it?

e) How many solutions to the area formula are there? Explain.

f) Find the solution that maximizes the area. What is the maximum possible area?

2. *Rich plans to fence in a rectangular kennel and use more fence to divide it into three equally sized sections for his dog Molly and her friends as shown. If he buys 450 feet of fence, find the dimensions of the kennel that maximize its area.* Dog: Nadya_Art/Shutterstock.com

a) Perform the quantitative analysis including labeling the diagram with variables.

b) Write formulas that relate the variables.

c) Substitute to get a formula for the area, ***A***, as in terms of one of the other variables. What kind of formula is it?

d) Find the solution that maximizes the area. What is the maximum possible area?

3. *The Asymptotes are having a concert where the number of tickets sold,* $\mathbf{N}$*, is a linear function of the ticket price,* $\mathbf{p}$ *dollars. The revenue,* $\mathbf{R}$*, is the total income generated by ticket sales, i.e.,* $\mathbf{R} = \mathbf{Np}$*. If* $\mathbf{N} = \mathbf{1900} - \mathbf{50p}$*. Find the ticket price that maximizes the revenue.*

a) The variables are defined in the problem. Make a table to summarize the quantitative analysis. Are there any constants?

b) Copy the (given) formulas that relate the variables.

c) Substitute to get a formula for the revenue, $\boldsymbol{R}$, in terms of one of the other variables.

d) Find the maximum possible revenue.

Self-Assessment Test 4: Quadratic Functions and Problem Solving

Instructions: For full credit, you must show how you did all of your calculations.
If a problem involves a function equation, show work using the equation.
Do NOT round in your calculations. Round final answers to the nearest hundredth if rounding is necessary.

1. *A large rectangular window has an area of 17,143 square centimeters, and its length is 20 centimeters less than 3 times its width. What are the dimensions of the window?*

a) Perform the quantitative analysis. Draw and label a diagram.

b) Translate the requirements into symbolic language. Write any other related formula(s).

c) Solve for the dimensions of the window.

2. *A box in the shape of a rectangular prism has a width of 8 inches and a length that is 1 foot more than its depth. If the volume of the box is 3074 cubic inches, what are the length and the depth of the box?*

a) Perform the quantitative analysis. Draw and label a diagram.

b) Translate the requirements into symbolic language. Write any other related formula(s).

c) Solve for the dimensions of the depth and the length of the box.

3. *The diagonal path across a rectangular field is 265 feet and the length of the field is 55 feet more than twice the width. What is the perimeter of the field?*

a) Perform the quantitative analysis. Draw and label a diagram.

b) Translate the requirements into symbolic language. Write any other related formula(s).

c) Solve for the dimensions of the field.

4. a) *A parabola has a minimum at* $(6, -2)$ *and an* x*-intercept at* $(10, 0)$. *What is the other* x*-intercept?*

b) *A parabola contains the point* $(-9, 3)$ *has axis of symmetry* $x = -6$. *Find another point on the parabola.*

c) *If a parabola has a horizontal intercept at* $(-12, 0)$ *and another at* $(8, 0)$, *what is its axis of symmetry?*

5. *Music promoters must decide how much to charge for each ticket to their next concert at the XL Center. Their money managers figure out that their profit in dollars for each show,* $\mathbf{P(x)}$, *depends on the ticket price in dollars,* $\mathbf{x}$, *and is given by the function:* $\mathbf{P(x) = -20x^2 + 2100x - 49000}$

a) How much profit do the promoters earn if they charge $42 for each ticket?

b) For this function, $P(20) = -15{,}000$. Explain what this means in the context of the situation.

c) Algebraically find the $P(x)$-intercept and explain its meaning in context.

d) What ticket price(s) should the promoters charge to break even?

e) What is the maximum profit that the promoters can earn for a concert?

6. For each table:

a) Determine whether table represents a relationship that is linear, exponential, quadratic, or none of those. You must show calculations to justify your answer.

b) IF the table is linear or exponential, write the function equation.

I.

x	y
0	2400
1	3600
2	5400
3	8100
4	12150

II.

x	y
0	3600
1	5400
2	7200
3	9000
4	10800

III.

x	y
0	–5
1	–2
2	7
3	22
4	43

IV.

x	y
0	0
1	3
2	8
3	15
4	24

7. *A college student launches a water balloon from the balcony of a building. The balloon's height off of the ground is a function of the amount of time after it is launched and is described by the equation* $h(t) = -16t^2 + 40t + 72$ *where* t *is time since launch in seconds and* $h(t)$ *is the height in feet.*

a) What was the initial height of the balloon when it was launched?

b) How high off the ground is the balloon after 1/2 second?

c) After how much time will the balloon reach 80 feet?

d) What is the peak height of the balloon?

e) When does it reach its peak height?

f) When will the balloon hit the ground?

Continued: *A college student launches a water balloon from the balcony of a building. The balloon's height off of the ground is a function of the amount of time after it is launched and is described by the equation*
$\boldsymbol{h(t) = -16t^2 + 40t + 72}$ *where* **t** *is time since launch in seconds and* $\mathbf{h(t)}$ *is the height in feet.*

g) Give the contextual (real-world) domain and range for this function.

h) Sketch a graph of the height function $h(t) = -16t^2 + 40t + 72$
Label axes and all of the important features/points of the function.

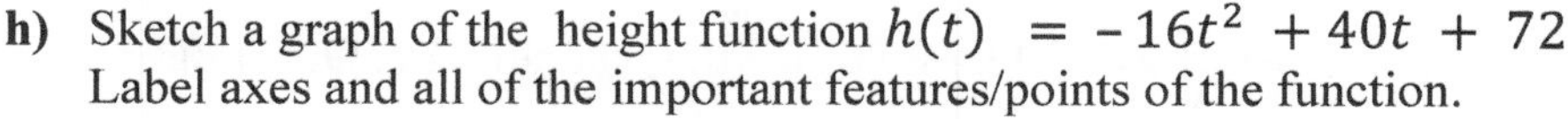

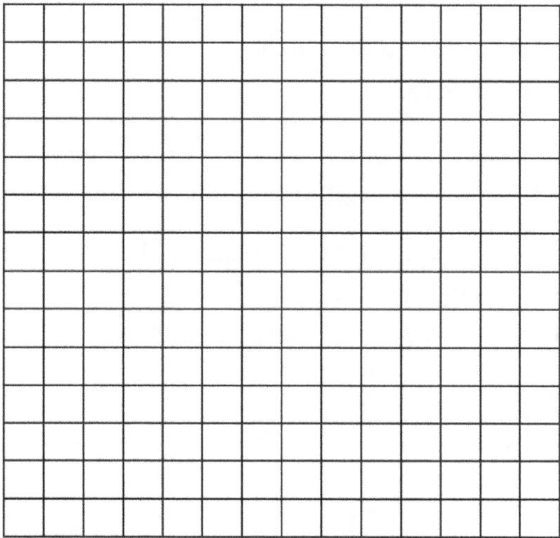

8. Explain how to tell whether a quadratic function has a maximum or a minimum from its equation in standard form $\boldsymbol{f(x) = ax^2 + bx + c}$ *without* graphing it.

9. Describe the number of horizontal intercepts each of the following function-types can have. Sketch graphs to illustrate all of the possibilities.

a) Linear

b) Exponential

c) Quadratic

Answer Key Test 4

1. $Length = 217$ cm, $Width = 79$ cm
2. $Depth = 14.5$ inches, $Length = 26.5$ inches
3. $Length = 247$ feet, $Width = 96$ feet, $Perimeter = 686$ feet
4. (a) $(2, 0)$; (b) $(-3, 3)$; (c) $x = -2$
5. (a) $P(42) = \$3920$; (b) If the ticket costs \$20, the promoters will *lose* \$15,000; (c) $P(0) = -\$49{,}000$, means that if the price of a ticket is \$0 (free) the promoters will lose \$49,000; (d) \$35 or \$70, in other words, $P(35) = 0\$ \; or \; P(70) = 4)$; (e) $P(52.5) = \$6{,}125$
6. I. Exponential $y = 24{,}000(1.5)^x$; II. Linear $y = 1800x + 3600$; III. Quadratic; IV. Quadratic
7. (a) $h(0 \; seconds) = 72 \; feet$; (b) $h\left(\frac{1}{2} \; sec.\right) = 88 \; feet$;
   (c) $h(\approx 0.22 \; sec.) = 80 \; feet$ and again at $h(\approx 2.28 \; sec.) = 80 \; feet$
   (d) peak height at $h(1.25) = 97$ feet; (e) 1.25 seconds after launch;
   (f) lands on the ground at ≈ 3.71 seconds after launch
   (f) Domain = $[0, 3.71]$ seconds; Range = $[0, 97]$ feet;
   (g) Graph not shown, $\boldsymbol{h(t)}$ feet – vertical axis label; $\boldsymbol{t}$ seconds – horizontal axis label; axis of symmetry: $t = 1.25$; suggested time scale 1 second for two squares; suggested height scale 20 feet for two square; important points (0,72), (1.25,97), (3.7,0); solid line.
8. Minimum for $\boldsymbol{a} > 0$ as parabola opens UP, and maximum for $\boldsymbol{a} < 0$ as parabola opens DOWN.
9. Horizontal intercepts : (Graphs not shown. See textbook for examples.)
   (a) Linear: one for increasing or decreasing lines, none for non-zero constant linear functions, infinitely many for the zero constant function $y = 0$;
   (b) Exponential: none as the x-axis is an asymptote;
   (c) Quadratic: one, two, or none